TWO ANDY GORAMS

NEW EDITION

Also by Ian Black

Who Wants to be a Glaswegian?
The (Completely Unofficial) Tartan Army Songbook
Weegies v. Edinbuggers

TWO ANDY GORAMS

THE FUNNIEST SCOTTISH FOOTBALL SONGS EVER

NEW EDITION

IAN BLACK

BLACK & WHITE PUBLISHING

First published 2002
New edition published 2003
by Black & White Publishing Ltd
99 Giles Street, Edinburgh EH6 6BZ

ISBN 1 902927 86 9

British Library Cataloguing in Publication Data:
A catalogue record for this book is available
from the British Library.

Every effort has been made to contact all copyright holders
of the material in this book. If you have any information
on any other copyright material contained herein,
please contact the publishers.

Printed and bound by Nørhaven Paperback A/S

CONTENTS

INTRODUCTION

A couple of years ago at Ibrox, when Andy Goram was being a bit more eccentric than was usual, even for him, a newspaper suggested that he was possibly suffering from schizophrenia. The following Saturday the terraces resounded to the chant, to the tune of Juantanamera:

Two Andy Gorams! There's only two Andy Gorams!

It is this kind of needle-sharp and non-PC wit that this book celebrates, whether it be the tribute to the efficacy of the motivational qualities of Martin O'Neill and the Catholic Church represented by the ditty below:

His name is Bob, Bobby Petta.
He was shite, now he's betta.
We took him to mass,
Now he's world class.
Walking in a Petta wonderland.

Or the story of a Rangers game a few years back, when foreign players were still pretty new. The manager took off Barry Ferguson, the only Scot in the team, and sent on another foreigner. The crowd instantly responded with, to the tune of 'Chirpy Chirpy Cheep Cheep':

Where's your Proddy gone? Where's your Proddy gone?

and continued:

Not far enough! Not far enough!

Stuart Cosgrove tells of when, as a lad in Perth, he used to sing *When the Saints Go Marching In*, one of the greatest songs of all time, because he's a St Johnstone supporter. He thought that every time he heard a gospel choir, Louis Armstrong, or whoever, singing it, that they were Saints fans too. How wrong he was. A wee while ago at McDiarmid Park, Scotland's first all-covered ground, where the fans used to sing:

We've got one, we've got two,
We've got three more stands than you.

the opposition were singing:

Have fun in Division One,
Have fun in Division One.

Mind you, it was only for the entire game.

There are plenty of other examples of this kind of thinking, but sometimes, especially if you are a 'Well fan, singing can be better than watching the game. I was at a stultifyingly boring game at Fir Park a decade or so back and somebody started to sing:

Ay, ay, ay, Tiswas *is better than* Swapshop.

Everybody in the crowd joined in, as it was patently true. The players were in knots, and the ref was laughing so hard that he couldn't even blow his whistle.

The book also contains a lot of the traditional songs and chants, though, by and large, I've left out the sectarian ones . . . unless they are funny. Humour is a great sociolgical leveller and

I'd rather be Bin Laden than a Tim

is of course completely interchangeable, and one of the continuing joys of living in the West of Scotland, though Hearts and Hibs have their own orange and green biases too, as you will discover, as do the teams in Dundee.

Have fun, and remember to sing when you are losing as well as when you are winning. You'll live longer.

For my Dad, who took me to my first Motherwell and my first Scotland games, and for my Mum, who is the best wee Mammy in human history.

And also for John (We are Leeds, we are Leeds, we are Leeds) Woad and Jacquie (Gonny gie us a brek with the Leeds song, John?) Shaw, who suggested this book because they wanted to read it.

Thanks

to everyone who wrote, e-mailed and poured songs, chants, obscenities and blasphemy down my phone. I've tried to mention everyone and if your name is missing it is probably because I subconsciously don't like you.

Alastair Nicholson, Ruary McGregor, Ally Maciver, Gordon Forsyth, Peter Speed, Gordon Johnstone, Will fae Swindon, Wullie Anderson, Martin Mitchell Ian Learmonth, Davie Carson, Mike McColl . . .

and dozens of fanzines, websites and anonymous correspondents as well as all the rest who contributed to this second edition.

Disclaimer

The views, comments and opinions contained in this book are entirely those of the fans and supporters of each club. In each case, the author has reproduced these as faithfully as possible and neither the author nor the publisher accepts any responsibility for the fans' vicious sense of humour, appalling rudeness or ready wit. Just as well professional footballers are paid a fortune if they get this kind of treatment every week, but the bucks, the burdz and the booze must be a comfort.

TWO ANDY GORAMS

ABERDEEN

FOUNDED: 1903
NICKNAME: THE DONS
BIGGEST WIN: 13-0 (PETERHEAD 1923)
BIGGEST LOSS: 0-8 (CELTIC 1965)
GROUND: PITTODRIE (WHICH, INCIDENTALLY,
MEANS DUNGHEAP) STADIUM
FANZINE: THE RED FINAL

*   *   *

He puts his lipstickon, his high heels on
Albertz is a tranny and he should be called Yvonne
Albertz is a tranny and he's coming out
Albertz is coming Out! Out! Out!
Oh! Albertz is a tranny
Oh! Albertz is a tranny
Oh! Albertz is a tranny
Albertz is coming out . . . Right soon!

First heard at the last Aberdeen v Rangers Cup Final.
Goes to the tune of 'The Hokey Cokey' and the final
four lines involve a strangely attractive hip-swinging

motion by the performers. The mighty Jorg is gone from Rangers but the song lives on, both in this format and with the inclusion of any other name that scans, like Fergy or Lorenzo used to.

Sensitive, or what?

I would rather shag a sheep than Mrs Mols.

And the women are as bad.

I'd rather shag a sheep than Michael Mols.

And now, a few new and old ones from the pride of Inverurie, Ally MacIver. He sent me these. Slainte, Ally!

"When AFC were playing Hertha Berlin a lot of good songs were emanating from the Irish Bar in the centre of Berlin. One that made me chuckle was when this little guy with grey hair and a beard was being carried out by his mate cause he had had too many shandies. He was being escorted out to:

Two Georgie Bests
There's only two Georgie Bests
Two Georgie Be-ests
There's only two Georgie Be-ests

Another from that night was sung about Gazza:

He goes out on a Friday night
gets fuckin' plastered
he drinks ten pints
and he beats his wife
He's a fat Geordie bastard

Aberdeen fans to Celtic fans at Pittodrie a few seasons back when they just couldn't get past Goram in OF matches . . .

"Cannae beat the Rangers,
Cannae beat the Rangers . . ."
(Over and over to the tune of na na na na na)

Their response was quite effective . . .

"Cannae beat the Celtic
cannae beat the Celtic . . ."

Much as this severely pissed me off I still laughed out loud!

To the Tims at Pittodrie:
Go home, to your Caravans
Go home, to your Caravans

Go home, to your Caravans
Go home, to your Caravans

To the Huns at Pittodrie,

Shall we have a
Shall we have a
Shall we have a wash for you?
Shall we have a wash for you?

Sung to the people on the hill who didn't want to pay to get into Almondvale:

Who's the minkers?
Who's the minkers?
Who's the minkers on the hill?
Who's the minkers on the hill?

For more vintage, how about when everyone held their right arm across the side of their face (so it looked like a trunk) and sang:

Davie Dodds, the elephant man, Da-a-a-vie Dodds, the elephant man

Eoin Jess Eoin Jess running down the wing
Eoin Jess Eoin Jess running down the wing
Feared by the Huns, loved by the reds
Eoin Jess, Eoin Jess, Eoin Jess

or alternatively

Eoin Jess Eoin Jess running down the wing
Eoin Jess Eoin Jess running down the wing
Crosses the ball, Shearer scores the goal
Eoin Jess, Eoin Jess, Eoin Jess

Ah . . . happy days

To the tune of Davy Crockett . . .

Born in a tenement in Aiberdeen,
the finest winger you've ever seen
Graham, Graham Leggate,
King of Pitt-od-er-ee

Another Dons fan sent this, chanted at Tannadice to Allan Combe:

Oh we bet u fucking hated Basil Brush
Oh we bet u fucking hated Basil Brush
Oh we bet u fucking hated, bet u fucking hated
We bet u fucking hated Basil Brush

Dons fans at Tannadice during 5-3 win:

Oh I'd rather be a brush than a Combe
Oh I'd rather be a brush than a Combe
Oh I'd rather be a brush
Rather be a brush
Rather be a brush than a Combe.

There is long-standing and all-too-real enmity between Aberdeen and Rangers fans which is sung of only to Celtic supporters:

We hate Rangers
We hate Rangers
We hate Rangers more than you!

Grammarians will no doubt point out that for precision and to convey exactly what is meant the song should end in do, but there's a nice ambivalence about it as it is and besides, nobody likes a smartass.

The Dons fans, also known as NEEPS, which is the acronym for North Eastern Ethnic Persons, have a nice line in self-deprecation and specialise in turning opposition slurs on their heads, with their own wee twist:

Sheep-shaggin baaaastards
Yes, we are sheep-shaggin baaaastards
Sheep-shaggin baaaastards
Yes, we are sheep-shaggin ba-a-a-astards.

ABERDEEN, ABERDEEN

A classic one this:

Aberdeen, Aberdeen, Aberdeen,
Aberdeen, Aberdeen, Aberdeeeen,
Aberdeen, Aberdeen, Aberdeeeen,
Aberdeeeeen, Aaaaabbeeeeerrrdddeeeeeeennn.

IT'S A GOAL

It's a goal, Duncan Shearer!
It's a goal, Duncan Shearer!
We're walking along
Singing a song
Walking in a Shearer wonderland.

Variation on a theme:

It's a goal, Robbie Winters!
It's a goal, Robbie Winters!
We're walking along
Singing a song
Walking in a Winters wonderland.

The mutton-pokers also sing 'The Northern Lights of Old Aberdeen', a maudlin song written by a wee old wifie who never saw Aberdeen, never mind the aurora borealis:

THE NORTHERN LIGHTS OF OLD ABERDEEN

When I was a lad, a tiny wee lad,
my mother said to me,
'Come see the Northern Lights my boy,
they're bright as they can be.'
She called them the heavenly dancers,
merry dancers in the sky,
I'll never forget that wonderful sight,
they made the heavens bright.

Chorus
The Northern Lights of Old Aberdeen,
mean home sweet home to me,
The Northern Lights of Aberdeen,
are what I long to see.
I've been a wanderer all of my life,
and many a sight I've seen,
Godspeed the day when I'm on my way,
to my home in Aberdeen.

I've wandered in many far off lands,
and travelled many a mile,
I've missed the folk I've cherished most,
the joy of a friendly smile.
It warms up the heart of a wanderer,
the clasp of a welcoming hand,
To greet me when I return,
home to my native land.

Chorus

Rival supporters counter with:

The Northern Lights of Old Aberdeen
Mean sweet fuck-all to me.
The Northern Lights of Aberdeen
Are no worth a bucket of pee.

And there are variations:

THE GLORIOUS DONS

When I was a lad, a bonnie wee lad,
My mither said tae me,
'Go see the Dons, the glorious Dons,
Down at Pit-odd-er-ie'.

They call them the heavenly dancers,
They're strong in attack and defence, (DEFENCE!)
And since that day, that glorious day,
I've been a supporter since.

Tune: 'You Are My Sunshine'

You're just a Weegie
A smelly Weegie
You're only happy on Giro day
Your Ma's a stealer
Your Da's a dealer
Please don't take my hubcaps away

Tune: 'When the Saints Go Marching In'

Oh when the Reds go steamin' in
Oh when the Reds go steamin' in
I want to be in that number
When the Reds go steamin' in

MOROCCAN ALL OVER THE WORLD

Here we go and here we go and here we go
With Belabed and with Zero
Here we go-o
Moroccan All Over the World

Tune: 'The Lord of the Dance'

Stand free wherever you may be
We are the famous Aberdeen
And we don't give a fuck whoever you may be
Cause we are the famous Aberdeen.

THE BEACH END BOYS

His name is Joe Harper, the cock of the North,
He plays at Pittodrie, just North of Kincorth,
He'll drink all your whisky and Newcastle Brown,
The Beach End Boys are in town

Na na na . . . na na na na na, na na na na na, Hoii !!!
Na na na na na, na na na na na, Hoii !!!
Na na na na na, na na na na na –
The Beach End Boys are in town !!!

SIGN ON

<u>Tune: 'You'll Never Walk Alone'</u>
<u>(sung mostly to Glaswegians)</u>

Sign on
Sign on
With hope in your heart
Cos you'll never get a job
You'll never get a job

YOU ARE MY SOLBERG

<u>Tune: 'You Are My Sunshine'</u>

You are my Solberg
My Thomas Solberg
You make me happy, when skies are grey
Fuck Amoruso, he's a wanker
Please don't take my Solberg away

WE HATE GLASGOW RANGERS

Tune: 'Land of Hope and Glory'

We hate Glasgow Rangers
We hate Celtic too
We hate Dundee United
But Aberdeen we love you

Altogether now

(Repeat indefinitely)

A few years back:

Who ate all the straw?
Who ate all the straw?
Dave McPherson, donkey bastard!
He ate all the straw!

WE'RE RED, YOU'RE DEAD

We're red, you're dead
We're bouncing on your head
We're Aberdeeeeeen

COME ON YOU REDS

Tune: 'Auld Lang Syne'

Come on you reds,
Come on you reds,
Come on you reds, come on,
Come on you reds,
Come on you reds,
Come on you reds, come on.

THE FAMOUS ABERDEEN

Tune: 'Yellow Submarine'

In a town beside the sea
Lies a fitba team called Aiberdeen
And we go to see them play
In the stadium Pittodrie

And we sing all of our songs
To show support for our beloved Dons
So we'll play for victory
And we'll be smiling all the way

Chorus
We all follow the famous Aberdeen
The famous Aberdeen
The famous Aberdeen
We all follow the famous Aberdeen
The famous Aberdeen
The famous Aberdeen

Only sung for the Old Firm, because of their Irish
and English affiliations, to the tune 'Juantanamera'

Wrong fucking country,
You're in the wrong fucking country,
Wrong fucking country.
You're in the wrong fucking country.

THE HITCHAM ZEROUALLI

Tune: 'The Hokey Cokey'

You put your left leg in
Your left leg out
In out
In out
You shake it all about

You do the Hitcham Zeroualli and you turn around
That's what it's all about

Oh, Hitcham Zeroualli
Oh, Hitcham Zeroualli
Oh, Hitcham Zeroualli
Knows what it's all about

The Don's European song:

SINGING A EUROPEAN SONG

We can sing, and we can play,
but Alex Ferguson, he knows the way
And we're gonna do it,
we're gonna do it,
we're gonna do it for you.
We're the Dons, from Aberdeen,
And we're the finest that's ever been.
And we're gonna do it for you,
And we're gonna do it for you.

McLeish and Miller,
And Strachan too,
will lead us forward,
and take us through.

And we're gonna do it,
we're gonna do it,
we're gonna do it for you.

We've taken our team into Europe,
Yes we have, oh-oh-oh yes we have,
All the way, every night and day,
singing a European song
oh oh All the way, every night and day.

We've taken our team into Europe
Yes we have, oh-oh-oh yes we have
All the way, every night and day,
singing a European song
oh oh All the way, every night and day,
singing a European . . .

And we're gonna do it,
we're gonna do it,
we're gonna do it for you.

We've taken our team into Europe
Yes we have, oh-oh-oh yes we have
All the way, every night and day,
singing a European song,
oh oh All the way, every night and day,
singing a European song.

And a final one from Ally:

We come from Aberdeen
We don't wear no blue or green
Cos there's
More to life than bigotry
We're proud to be red white and free
Oh yes the
Northern Lights shine bright on us
We love sheep
What's the fuss???
And Angus the Bull
He's so damn cool
He's King of the Park
dadum dum dum

and repeat

AIRDRIE

(NOW AIRDRIE UNITED)

FOUNDED: 1878
NICKNAME: THE DIAMONDS
BIGGEST WIN: 15-1 (DUNDEE WANDERERS 1894)
BIGGEST LOSS: 1-11 (HIBS 1959)
GROUND: SHYBERRY EXCELSIOR
(OR, TO THE FANS, NEW BROOMFIELD)
FANZINE: ONLY THE LONELY

* * *

He's black!
He's gay!
He plays for Air-der-aayy,
Fashanu, Fashanu!

Fash the Bash had his own song:

Came for the ball boys,
You only came for the ball boys.

KEN EADIE

Ken Eadie, Ken Eadie, he's got ginger hair,
Ken Eadie, Ken Eadie, he is always there,
He gets the ball, he scores a goal,
Ken Eadie, Ken Eadie, Ken Eadie.

AIRDERIE IS WONDERFUL

Oh, Airderie, is wonderful
Airderie is wonderful
It's full of drugs, hoors and Buckfast
Airderie is wonderful

DIAMONDS ARE A BOY'S BEST FRIEND

A punch on the beak could be non-accidental,
Causing it to break or bend,
So when you see Section B going mental,
Being a Diamond is a boy's best friend.

<u>Tune: 'Bluebells Are Blue'</u>

Oh, diamonds are red
Oh, diamonds are red
Oh, diamonds are red
Oh, diamonds are red

And so on till your neighbour smashes your face in.

ALBION ROVERS

Founded: 1882
Nickname: The Rovers
Biggest win: 12-0 (Airdriehill 1887)
Biggest loss: 1-11 (Partick Thistle 1993)
Stadium: Cliftonhill,
aka Cliftonhell to visitors
Fanzine: All Things Bright and Beautiful

* * *

Here's a blast from the past. Nobody seems to know who wrote it or the tune:

It's a good wee team
It's a grand wee team
It's a game wee team
We call The Rovers
They're the champions o' the world
And when our banner is unfurled
You will see that we're the Albion Rovers

And now, a certain change of pace . . . and century.

We've a certain reputation for seducing little boys
For mugging old age pensioners and for
stealing children's toys
We're the perverts of our nation we're the
*c**** you'll never see*
We're the dirty foul-mouthed bastards of the Rovers AFC

In the land of Monty Python in the land within a dream
Lies a six foot Zulu warrior being fucked by
a Royal Marine
We're the perverts of our nation we're
*the c**** you'll never see*
We're the dirty foul-mouthed bastards of the Rovers AFC

ALLOA

FOUNDED: 1878
NICKNAME: THE WASPS
BIGGEST WIN: 9-2 (FORFAR 1933)
BIGGEST LOSS: 0-10 (DUNDEE 1937)
GROUND: RECREATION PARK
FANZINE: HIY SERR

* * *

They too have a nice line in pleasantries. They sing:

We are Alloa, super Alloa,
No one likes us and we care,
We are trying to be nice folk,
And to teach the world to share.

ARBROATH

FOUNDED: 1878
NICKNAME: THE RED LICHTIES
BIGGEST WIN: 36-0 (BON ACCORD 1885)
BIGGEST LOSS: 1-9 (CELTIC 1993)
GROUND: GAYFIELD PARK
FANZINE: THE GAYFIELD DECEIVERS

* * *

SING WHEN WE'RE FISHIN

Sing when we're fishin
We only sing when we're fishing
Sing when we're fishin
We only sing when we're fishing

Only in Arbroath. A nice crisp, dry Sauvignon, one trusts:

> *Smokies and wine*
> *Smokies and wine*
> *Come on Come on*

They have an organisation called The 36-0 Club and they sing this when Aberdeen are in town:

> *The Northern Lights of Old Aberdeen*
> *36-Nil! 36-Nil!*

AYR UNITED

FOUNDED: 1910
NICKNAME: THE HONEST MEN
BIGGEST WIN: 11-1 (DUMBARTON 1952)
BIGGEST LOSS: 0-9 (RANGERS 1929, HEARTS 1931,
THIRD LANARK 1954)
GROUND: SOMERSET PARK
FANZINE: THE MONKEY'S HEID

* * *

THE MONKEY'S HEID

Tune: 'Yellow Submarine'

Oh in the land,
Where I was born,
There was a team . . . called Ayr FC.
And they were black, and they were white,
They fucked the Killie . . . cos they were shite.
AND WE SAID,
Bobby Williamson's got a fucking monkey's heid,
A fucking monkey's heid, a fucking monkey's heid.

Bobby Williamson's got a fucking monkey's heid,
A fucking monkey's heid, a fucking monkey's heid.

IN YOUR KILLIE SLUMS

In your Killie slums.
You look in your bucket for something to eat.
You see a dead rat and you think it's a treat.
In your Killie slums.

In your Killie slums.
You kick all your rubbish out into the street.
You fight like fuck over a wee bit of meat.
In your Killie slums.

In your Killie slums.
You shit on the carpet, you pish in the bath.
You finger your gran 'cause you think it's a laugh.
In your Killie slums.

In your Killie slums.
Your mother's a whore and your dad's in the nick.
You can't get a job 'cause your so fuckin' thick.
In your Killie slums.

PAPER HANKIES

Tune: 'Paper Roses'

You don't realise the way your eyes deceive you
You think the Ayrshire Killie's a football team
But when you see them playing Ayr United
You realise your hopes are just a dream

(Everyone starts waving paper hankies in the air . . .)

Paper hankies, paper hankies,
Let our paper hankies wipe your tears,
For you're only imitations,
Ayrshire's number one wear black and white!

PAPER ROSES (AYR UNITED REMIX!!)

You can shove your paper roses up yer arse,
RIGHT UP!
You can shove your paper roses up yer arse,
RIGHT UP,
You can shove your paper roses,
Your shitey paper roses,
You can shove your paper roses up yer arse,
RIGHT UP!

BERWICK RANGERS

FOUNDED: 1881
NICKNAME: THE BORDERERS
BIGGEST WIN: 8-1 (FORFAR ATHLETIC 1965,
VALE OF LEITHEN 1966)
BIGGEST LOSS: 1-9 (HAMILTON 1980)
GROUND: SHIELFIELD PARK
FANZINE: FROM THE VALE TO THE HARROW

* * *

They have a special chant for Morton supporters, which goes:

Your mother is your sister
Your sister is your mother

To which the Morton people stand, shrug their shoulders and say 'So?' and 'And?' and 'What is your point, caller?' . . .

BRECHIN CITY

FOUNDED: 1906
NICKNAME: THE CITY
BIGGEST WIN: 12-1 (THORNHILL 1926)
BIGGEST LOSS: 0-10 (AIRDRIE, ALBION ROVERS,
COWDENBEATH, ALL 1937-38)
GROUND: GLEBE PARK
FANZINE: THE HEDGE CLIPPINGS

* * *

The only song that Brechin fans claim as their own is
the following:

I can't read and I can't write,
But it don't really matter,
Because I am a Brechinite,
And I can drive a tractor.

There is a song about Brechin which has been sung on the odd occasion:

REEKIN IN BRECHIN

Tune: 'Roamin in the Gloamin'

Oh, reekin in Brechin,
We were ayeways steamin,
You were on the voddy,
Ah was on the wine.
We've sat in different jiles,
And that's why we've got piles,
We were ayeways reekin in Brechin.

CELTIC

FOUNDED: 1888
NICKNAMES: THE BHOYS,
THE TIM MALLOYS, THE TIMS
BIGGEST WIN: 11-0 (DUNDEE 1895).
BIGGEST LOSS: 0-8 (MOTHERWELL [YES!] 1937)
GROUND: CELTIC PARK, AKA PARKHEAD
FANZINES: NOT THE VIEW, THE CELT,
PLUS MANY MORE

* * *

A simple, but menacing, one for a start:

Bobo's gonna get ya
Bobo's gonna get ya

And a new one celebrating debt, a somewhat unusual
Celtic development. And it isn't about Celtic. It was
sent to me by Micky Ross via David Lang:

Borrow borrow we will borrow millions
Anywhere everywhere we will borrow on

Dundee, Hamilton, we'd even tap the Vatican
If we go to Dublin we will borrow there

Another from the same stable.

Altogether now! The cry was no more spending
No more spending or we'll die, die, die
With cap in hand and millions owed
We'll sell old Derry's walls

For there's not a bank like the Bank of Scotland
No not one and there never shall be one
The bank manager knows all about our troubles
We will sell sell sell till there's no one left
Oh for there's not a bank like the Bank of Scotland
No not one and there never shall be one

And yet another. Is there no end to this *schadenfreude?*

Hello hello we're 80 million in debt
Hello hello we're not insolvent yet
We're up to our knees in Murray's debt
Sell players or we'll die
For we are the poorest club in Scotland

It would appear not.

TELL ALL THE HUNS YOU KNOW

Tune: 'The Entertainer'

Tell all the Huns you know
They'll never sell Ricksen or Flo
They'll never sell Ricksen, never sell Ricksen,
never sell Ricksen or Flo . . .
Half price!

And, just before the planting of the most senior royal:

Tell all the Huns you know
The Queen Mother's deid, the Pope's no.
The Queen Mother's deid, the Queen Mother's deid,
The Queen Mother's deid,
The Pope's no.

And when Celtic made it to Seville, the floodgates opened:

Tell all the Huns you smell
We'll be staying in a Spanish hotel
It was just after Easter we pumped Boavista
and humped youse at Ibrox as well.

We'll be in Seville,
And you'll be watching the Bill
You'll be down at the chip shops,
While we're wearing flip-flops

Tell all the huns ya know,
that we're going to Spain and you're no,
as you shag the lodge goat,
on our lilos we'll float,
cos we're going to Spain and your no!

There was also:

We don't mean to tease
But its 90 degrees
And the San Miguel's starting to flow.

Tune: 'You Are My Sunshine'

You are my Larsson, my Henrik Larsson
You make me happy when skies are grey
We went for Shearer
But he's a wanker
Please don't take my Larsson away

LUBO'S SONG

Tune: 'Delilah'

I saw the light in the night as I passed by old Ibrox
I saw the flickering shadow of despair on the blind
Deep from the Blue Room
Came a cry from a man who was lost
Going out of his mind

Why? Why? Why? Moravcik
Why? Why? Why? Moravcik
I could see . . . that Slovak was so cruel to me
Now I am lost with a team that no man can free

At break of day as they drove Dick away in a white van
I looked into the Blue Room . . . the Blue Room was bare
I stood there laughing . . . a ha a ha ah a ha a ha
(laughter to the tune of The Billy Boys)
No Mr Sheen, there's no trophies to clean
There's nae mair

Why? Why? Why? Moravcik
Why? Why? Why? Moravcik
So, before, old Dick gets slung out the door
Forgive him, Moravcik, he just couldn't face any more
Forgive him, Moravcik, he just couldn't face any more

At a Celtic Supporters Trust evening there was a nice wee woman called Cath who kept saying that she wanted to sing 'Bobby's Girl'. The organisers were a bit chary, as they thought that it was going to be some dirge about Bobby Sands. Cath lost patience near the end of the night, got up, grabbed the mike, and, to the chorus of the 1963 hit for Susan Maugham (the one that goes: *I wanna be . . . Bobby's girl*), she sang:

Rang rings round Ricksen
Made a c*** of Konterman

THE CELTIC SONG

Hail, Hail, the Celts are here
What the hell do we care
What the hell do we care
Hail, Hail, the Celts are here
What the hell do we care now . . .

For it's a grand old team to play for
For it's a grand old team to see
And if you know the history
It's enough to make your heart go
Nine-in-a-row

We don't care what the animals say
What the hell do we care
For we only know
That there's going to be a show
And Glasgow Celtic will be there

To which is often added, by the opposition:

Selling the programmes

HAMPDEN IN THE SUN

Chorus
Oh Hampden in the Sun,
Celtic 7 Rangers 1,
That was the score when it came time up,
The Tim Malloys had won the cup.

I see Tully running down the line,
He slips the ball past Valentine,
It's nodded down by 'Teazy Weazy',
And Sammy Wilson makes it look so easy.

Chorus

I see Mochan beating Shearer,
The League Cup is coming nearer,
He slams in an impossible shot,
The Rangers team has had their lot.

Chorus

Over comes a very high ball,
Up goes McPhail above them all,
The ball and Billy's head have met,
A lovely sight the ball is in the net.

Young Sam Wilson has them rocked,
But unluckily his shot was blocked,
Then big Bill with a lovely lob,
Makes it look such an easy job.

Chorus

Now here is Mochan on the ball,
He runs around poor Ian McColl,
Wee George Niven takes a daring dive,
But Smiler Mochan makes it number five.

Chorus

Down the middle runs Billy McPhail,
With John Valentine on his tail,
With a shot along the ground,
The cup's at Parkhead safe and sound.

Chorus

Here comes Fernie, cool and slick,
He ambles up to take the kick,
He hits it hard and low past Niven,
The Tims are in their Seventh Heaven.

BYE BYE RANGERS

Yo ho ho, off we go
What do you know, it's nine in a row
Bye bye Rangers
Celtic's on the ball again, on the way to make it ten
Bye bye Rangers
You can talk about your great defenders
Sing and shout about your No Surrender
But let us give you this wee tip
We'll be there for the league and the cup
Rangers bye bye
Yo ho ho, off we go
What do you know, it's nine in a row
Bye bye Rangers

Celtic's on the ball again, on the way to make it ten
Bye bye Rangers
You can talk about your great defenders
Sing and shout about your No Surrender
But let us give you this wee tip
We'll be there for the league and the cup
Rangers bye bye
But let us give you this wee tip
We'll be there for the league and the cup
Rangers bye bye

FOUR LEAF CLOVER

Chorus
With a four leaf clover on my breast,
And the green and white upon my chest,
It's such a joy for us to see,
For they play football the Celtic way.

Verse
It's been ten years, long time indeed,
We stood with pride and we took defeat,
Our beloved team, our ancient ground,
Has been rebuilt, a club reborn.

Chorus

McCann he rode the winds of change,
And the things he brought will long remain,
A phoenix rising, a house of steel,
And 60,000 Celtic dreams.

Chorus

The work is done and the stage is set,
The Celtic dream can now be met,
In a sea of dreams, we're here today,
Lets sit and watch the Champions play

THIS LAND IS YOUR LAND

Chorus
This land is your land, this land is my land
From the northern highlands to the western islands
From the hills of Kerry to the streets of (Free) Derry
This land was made for you and me

As I was walking by the Shannon water
Hand in hand with my little daughter
The church bells ringing, and the children singing
This land was made for you and me

Chorus

So I walked her home by the old church steeple
Proud of my country, proud of my people
Of the men who tried there, of the men who died there
singing
This land is made for you and me

Chorus

Then I climbed a mountain, saw the crystal fountain
And heard a great roar from the rocky sea shore
Her eyes were gleaming, she cried oho Daddy
This land was made for you and me

OVER AND OVER

Oh! over and over, we will follow you,
Over and over, we will see you through,
We're Celtic supporters, faithful through and through,
And over and over, we will follow you.

If you go to Germany, you will see us there,
France or Spain its all the same,
We'll go any where,
We'll be there to cheer you,
As you travel round,
You can take us anywhere, we won't let you down.

Oh! over and over, we will follow you,
Over and over, we will see you through,
We're Celtic supporters, faithful through and through,
And over and over, we will follow you.

If you go to Lisbon, we'll go once again,
In Zaire you'll find us there calling out your name,
When you need supporting, you will always know,
We'll be right there with you, every where you go.

Oh! over and over, we will follow you,
Over and over, we will see you through,
We're Celtic supporters, faithful through and through,
And over and over, we will follow you.

WILLIE MALEY

Chorus
Oh Willie Maley was his name,
He brought some great names to the game,
When he was the boss at Celtic Park.
Taught them how to play football,
He made the greatest of them all,
Gallagher and Quinn have left their mark.

And they gave us James McGrory and Paul McStay,
They gave us Johnstone, Tully, Murdoch, Auld and Hay,

And most of the football greats,
Have passed through Parkhead's gates,
All to play football the Glasgow Celtic way.
In '38 there was a show,
And Glasgow was the place to go,
A model of the Tower was football's prize.
England sent four of the best,
They didn't meet with much success,
Because the trophy ended up in Paradise.

Chorus

Well Coronation time was here,
Fifty three, that was the year,
Another four from England met their doom.
They said we'll have to try again,
But like before it was in vain,
Because the Cup is in the Parkhead trophy room.

Chorus

Well fourteen years had gone and so,
To Portugal we had to go,
To play the team that Italy adored.
Celtic went out to attack,
They won the Big Cup and they brought it back,
The first time it had been on British shores.

Now 21 years to that day,
With pride, it's our Centenary,
And we're among the honours once again.
Six million pounds the huns did spend,
But Souness found it was in vain,
Because the Celtic are the Champions again.

Chorus

And now in 1995,
It feels good to be alive,
And we're about to celebrate again.
The fans all cry out for Pierre,
He rises up into the air,
And brings the Scottish Cup to Paradise.

Chorus

THE CORONATION CUP

Said Lizzie to Philip as they sat down to dine,
'I've just had a note from a good friend of mine.
His name is big Geordie, he's loyal and true,
And his big dirty nose is a bright shade of blue.
He says that the Rangers are right on their game,

And he asks for a trophy to add to their fame.
We'll send them a trophy that the Rangers can win,'
Said Philip to Lizzie, 'Watch the Celts don't step in.'
Said Lizzie to Philip 'They don't stand a chance,
I'll send up my Gunners to lead them a dance.
With the Celtic defeated, the way will be clear,
And a trophy for the Rangers in my crowning year.'
Alas, and alas, for the wearers of blue,
The Celts beat the Arsenal and the Manchester too,
Beat Hibs in the final, and lo and behold,
All of Hampden was covered in green, white and gold,
Said Lizzie to Philip when she heard the news,
'So tell me dear Philip, for you ought to know,
How to beat Glasgow Celtic and keep them below.'
Said Philip to Lizzie, 'There's only one way,
And I've known the secret for many a day.
To beat Glasgow Celtic, you'll have to deport,
All the fighting mad Irish that give them support.'

CELTIC IS THE NAME

In Glasgow town we have a team
And Celtic is the name
We've beaten Rangers and Milan
For Celtic know the game
And if you don't believe me boys
Then come and see us play
For Glasgow Celtic, up the Celtic
Beats the world today
For Glasgow Celtic, up the Celtic
Beats the world today

We are a famous football team
I'm sure you all agree
We've played them all, the big and small
From Lisbon to Dundee
And if you don't believe me, boys
Then this to you I say
Come up the Parkhead, dear old Parkhead
Celtic leads the way
Come up the Parkhead, dear old Parkhead
Celtic leads the way

THE FIELDS OF ATHENRY

By a lonely prison wall,
I heard a young girl calling,
'Michael they have taken you away,
For you stole Trevelyan's corn,
So the young might see the morn,
Now a prison ship lies waiting in the bay.'

Chorus
Low lie the Fields of Athenry
Where once we watched the small, free birds fly,
Our love was on the wing,
We had dreams and songs to sing,
It's so lonely round the Fields of Athenry.

By a lonely prison wall,
I heard the young man calling,
'Nothing matters Mary when you are free,
'Gainst the famine and the crown,
I rebelled they cut me down,
Now you must raise our child with dignity.'

Chorus

By a lonely harbour wall,
She watched the last star falling

As the prison ship sailed out against the sky
Now she'll wait and hope and pray,
For her love in Botany Bay
It's so lonely round the Fields of Athenry

Tom Shields has a veggie meat substitute version of
this which goes:

For you stole Trevelyan's Quorn

But he says that most veggies can't sing for tofu.

CLYDE

FOUNDED: 1878
NICKNAME: THE BULLY WEE
BIGGEST WIN: 11-1 (COWDENBEATH 1951)
BIGGEST LOSS: 0-11 (DUMBARTON 1879,
RANGERS 1880)
GROUND: BROADWOOD STADIUM
FANZINE: THE WEE BULLY

* * *

There were no Clyde songs in the first edition, a situation that has been rectified (and how) by a young friend called Richie. Here goes:

SONG OF THE CLYDE

I sing of a team that fills me with pride
The name of the team is the Bully Wee Clyde
Of all Scottish teams they are dearest tae me
They've won everywhere frae Dumfries tae Dundee
They've beaten the Celtic, The Hibs and the Hearts
The Rangers and Thistle, they've swept frae the park

So come down tae Shawfield, you'll know I've not lied
When I tell you the greatest of teams is the CLYDE.

Chorus
Oh The Clyde, The Clyde, the bully Wee Clyde
The name of them thrills me and fills me with pride
And I'm satisfied what e'er may betide
The greatest of teams is the Bully Wee Clyde.

2
I'll be doon at Shawfield come hail or come shine
Supporting the team I will always call mine
Whether winning or losing, if up or if down
You'll still hear me shouting all over the town
I'll follow them East and I'll follow them West
Tae the North or the South still its "my team's the best"
So come down tae Shawfield you'll know I've not lied
When I tell you the greatest of teams is the Clyde.

Chorus

3
The year we first started, Eighteen Seventy Eight
Little did they know that we'd soon become great
All over the country we'd spread far and wide
The name and the colours o' the Bully Wee Clyde
we've taken some glory, been down and been up

Three times we have taken oor ain Scottish Cup
There's no one can tell what the future will be
But as lang as I live it will be Clyde for me.

Chorus

1, 2, 3

Chorus

And it's one 1,2,3 Cheering for the Bully Wee.
And its 4,5,6 Wi the team up tae their tricks
and its 7,8,9 Now they're playing fine
It's another goal.

1.
There's a team they call the Clyde
who will fill your heart wi' pride
Dressed up in their Red and Black
wi' an 'L' sign on their back
Wi' a winger and a keeper
an a great big carpet sweeper,
It's the Bully Wee

Chorus

2.

They have a large support
Just three camels and a goat
And an ostrich with a feather
an a dirty chami' leather,
Then there's you an' me
And the ball boy he makes three,
It's the Bully Wee.

Chorus

3.

Have you ever stood alone,
wi' a pie up in the stand,
Screaming at the ref.
Then it flies out o' yer hand,
and it hits him in the mooth,
just before you shouted duck.
Well its just his luck.

Chorus

4.

Then he blows the final whistle
and ye've beaten Partick Thistle,
An your feeling oh so proud,
that your singing right out loud

An your jumping up and down,
an you feel a silly clown,
'Cause you're all alone.

Chorus

5.

There was the day that ah was wed
ah did not go home to bed,
but down tae Shawfield Park
for a cuddle in the dark,
but the misses took the huff
she said I had no love
Except for Clyde.

Chorus

6.

Well maybe she is right,
so we started a wee fight
An I punched her oan the jaw,
so she went hame tae her maw,
But noo I'm quite ecstatic
I'm a single Clyde fanatic,
Come on the Clyde.

Chorus

But I'm sure the time is near,
let us give a great big cheer,
For the team that we support,
As you know we really ought,
Let us join in the chorus
t'was especially written for us

THE FAMOUS BULLY WEE

We are the famous Bully Wee
We hate the Jags and we hate Airdrie
We don't give a fuck, wherever we may be
Cause we are the Famous Bully Wee!

FOREVER AND EVER

Forever and ever, we'll follow the Clyde,
the Bully Wee Clyde, yer mother's pride,
For we will be mastered (by who) by no Thistle bastard,
we'll keep the Clyde flag flying high,
so bring on yer Hibs yer Hearts and Thistle,
fuck yer boys in royal blue and green,
for we'll shut the bastards up when we lift
the Scottish Cup,
for Clyde are the greatest football team.

JOHNNIE LAMBIE

Cheer up Johhny Lambie
Oh what can it be
To a sad Thistle Bastard
and a shite football team!

GLORY GLORY

Glory! Glory!
Gypsy Army
As the Clyde go marching on! ON! ON!

QUE SERA SERA

Que Sera Sera
What ever we'll be we'll be
We'll follow the Bully Wee
Que Sera Sera

THISTLE HATERS

We hate Thistle and we hate Thistle
We hate Thistle and we hate Thistle

We hate Thistle and we hate Thistle
We are the Thistle . . . Haters!
We are the Thistle . . . Haters!

FUCK 'EM ALL

Fuck 'em all
Fuck 'em all
Yer Rangers yer Celtic them all
For we won't be mastered by no Thistle Bastard
Thats why we sing Fuck 'em all
Fuck 'em all
Fuck 'em all

WE HATE . . .

We hate Glasgow Rangers
We hate Celtic too, (They're Shite!)
We hate Partick Thistle
But The Clyde we love you
(Altogether now!)

SHAWFIELD BOYS

Oh we come from the Shawfield, They call us the Clyde
We'll kill any bastard that tries to get wide
We'll drink all yer whisky, Yer Newcastle brown
The Shawfield boys are in town!
nana, nana na na, nana nana na

OOH! OOH! GYPSY ARMY!
OOH! OOH! GYPSY ARMY

This one is usually kept for cup games, I'm told.

Tune: 'I Do Like to be Beside the Seaside'

All the champions they play at Shawfield
All the stars they play for Clyde
Because there's something about the football
That makes us famous far and wide
Scoring's easy, bright and breezy
Oh they're their supporters pride and joy
for we've all our minds made up
who will win the Scottish cup
Oh it's the Clyde, the Bully Wee Clyde

IN MEMORIAM:
CLYDEBANK

FOUNDED: 1965
KILLED 2002 BY THE SCOTTISH LEAGUE
NICKNAME: THE BANKIES, THE PAPER HANKIES
BIGGEST WIN: 8-1 (ARBROATH 1977)
BIGGEST LOSS: 1-9 (GALA FAIRYDEAN 1965)

* * *

Tune: 'One of Those Songs'

It's one of those feelings you get now and then,
We'll beat the Dumbarton again and again,
We'll drink all your whisky, your Newcastle Brown.
The Bankie boys are in town.

IF I HAD THE WINGS OF A SPARROW

If I had the wings of a sparrow,
And I had the arse of a crow,
I'd fly over Firhill tomorrow,
And shit on the bastards below, below,
Shit on, shit on, shit on the bastards below.

This one is titled:

A TRIBUTE TO CLYDEBANK'S TOUGH TACKLING 70'S FULL-BACK

I wonder what it's about.

Oh they called him Norrie Hall, Norrie Hall
Oh they called him Norrie Hall, Norrie Hall
Oh they called him Norrie Hall
Cause he's only got one leg
Oh they called him Norrie Hall, Norrie Hall

Oh they put him on a roof, on a roof
Oh they put him on a roof, on a roof
Oh they put him on a roof
Cause they thought he was a slater
Oh they called him Norrie Hall, Norrie Hall

Oh they put him down a stank, down a stank
Oh they put him down a stank, down a stank
Oh they put him down a stank
Cause they thought he was a plumber
Oh they called him Norrie Hall, Norrie Hall

Oh they put him down a pit, down a pit
Oh they put him down a pit, down a pit
Oh they put him down a pit
And they covered him with gravel
Oh they called him Norrie Hall, Norrie Hall

Repeat verse 1 indefinitely.

A song for Partick Thistle:

CHEER UP JOHNNY LAMBIE

Cheer up Johhny Lambie
Oh what can it mean
To a shite football manager
Of a shite football team

And they used to sing:

We build ships, sewing machines,
We build famous football teams,
We're the Bankies from Kilbowie Park,
Thank fuck

COWDENBEATH

FOUNDED: 1881
NICKNAME: THE BLUE BRAZIL
BIGGEST WIN: 12-0 (ST JOHNSTONE 1928)
BIGGEST LOSS: 1-11 (CLYDE 1951)
GROUND: CENTRAL PARK
FANZINE: WHEN THE SUN SHINES

* * *

I don't know who christened Cowdenbeath the Blue Brazil, but he or she was at least half wrong. I'm told that the fans sing this, though it is difficult to understand them as their tongues are imbedded so far in their cheeks.

Tune: 'Brazil'

Brazil, it's just like watching Brazil
It's just like watching Brazil
It's just like watching Brazil
Brazil etc, etc

Here's one that I was sent by Bzzzz, a TA chum. He says that it is: "possibly the oldest chant in Scottish fitba", and claims that it was invented at Cowden-beath. It goes:

Fer fucks SAKE!

They also sing a wee ditty I've heard nowhere else, to the tune of 'When the Saints':

THERE WAS A COO

There was a coo, on yonder hill,
(everyone else: 'On yonder hill')
There was a coo on yonder hill,
(everyone else: 'On yonder hill')
It's no there noo, it must have shiftit,
There was a coo, on yonder hill.

They used to have a shed at Central Park, a rickety thing that blew away one night in a storm, and it is remembered in another of their songs, which goes:

When the sun shines on the Cowshed
And the ball goes in the net
You will hear the Cowden Boot Boys
Going off their fuckin heads

Lots of visiting fans sing this one, particularly East Fife, whose fanzine editor, Mike McColl, made it up. Berwick Rangers and Stirling Albion seem to enjoy singing it too.

<u>Tune: 'The Addams Family'</u>

They're dirty and they're smelly
They're fae up near Lochgelly
They've never seen a telly
The Cowden family

This is followed by a sort of sideways shuffle dance step while going: 'Duh-du-der-uh'

The girls have got moustaches
They've all got nasty rashes
And nae c*** ever waashes
The Cowden Family

Chorus

The Blue Brazil were not too chuffed. This is the reply of their fanzine editor:

THE METHIL FAMILY

These people come from Methil
They think they're in fine fettle
It's obvious they'll just have to settle
For being a Methil family

Their fanzine editor gets called Mike
And he really should get on his bike
For his comments we did not like
From this son of a Methil family

He thinks his comments do not matter
About Cowden folks that don't use watter
But we'll have his balls upon a platter
And no more Methil families

He just obviously disnae think
That we can go and use a sink
What do you expect from a Bayview wid-tink
And an ozone unfriendly Methil family

Now if you're driving out of Leven
Watch out for people drinking semen
And a team that concedes seeven
And also a Methil family

DUMBARTON

FOUNDED: 1872
NICKNAME: THE SONS
BIGGEST WIN: 13-1 (KIRKINTILLOCH 1888)
BIGGEST LOSS: 1-11 (ALBION ROVERS 1926)
GROUND: OFFICIALLY IT IS STRATHCLYDE HOMES
STADIUM BUT ALL THE FANS CALL IT THE ROCK
FANZINE: CLOCK AROUND THE ROCK

* * *

One from the Seventies, when Boghead used to be full most weeks.

If you go down to Boghead today
You're in for big surprise
If you go down to Boghead today
You'd better go in disguise
For Cushley's there, the human bear
A dirty big bastard wi' dark curly hair
Today's the day that Cushley has his picnic

DUNDEE

FOUNDED: 1893
NICKNAME: THE DARK BLUES
BIGGEST WIN: 10-0 (ALLOA, DUNFERMLINE,
BOTH 1957)
BIGGEST LOSS: 0-11 (CELTIC 1895)
GROUND: DENS PARK
FANZINES: EH MIND O' GILLIE,
IT'S HALF PAST FOUR AND WE'RE 2-0 DOWN

* * *

Let's start with the traditional:

There's only one United
And that's a fucking biscuit

PROVY ROAD

Howay the lads, you should have seen us coming,
We're only here to drink your beer and shag your fucking
women,
All the lads and lasses should have been delighted,
Walking down the Provy Road,
To kick fuck out United!

The Pole, The Pole,
He's Dariusz the Pole,
He get's the ball,
And scores a goal,
Dariusz the Pole.

ANDO

Fuck off Ando,
Fuck off Ando,
Fuck off Ando,
Fuck off Ando.

This is from my chum Kosmic, who went back to Dundee to ask his mum for the words. It is from around the early Sixties.

UP WI' THE BONNETS

Tune: traditional

You can sing of your glories of teams you have seen
From the Saints to the Dons up in old Aberdeen
But in all the whole world there's but one team for me
It's the brave boys who wear the dark blue of Dundee

Chorus
Let the proud Rangers sing of the records they hold
Let Celtic acclaim their heroes of old
We will follow and follow on land and on sea
For the brave boys who wear the dark blue of Dundee

There's many a battle been fought on this field
There's many a team learned that Dundee never yield
But though on occasion defeat we must know
We will rise up again and defeat every foe

Chorus

There's Robertson, Penman, Alan Gilzean
There's Cousins and Smith, they're the finest you've seen
And a defence that stood steady, heroic and sure
Liney, Hamilton, Cox, Seith, Wishart and Ure

Chorus

And a somewhat scary one for Glaswegians

Tune: 'Bohemian Rhapsody'

Is this the real life, is it the methodone?
Stuck in the Gorbals, two bob fur the telephone?
Open yer wine an' talk wi' a whine like me.
Um just a weeji, gie us yer Sunny D.
Cos I'll chib yer pal, rip yer Da;
Slash yer dug, ride yer ma!

Any way the Clyde flows
Disnae really matter tae me . . . tae me.

Haw Maw, just chibbed some bam,
Buckie bottle tae the heid,
An noo the fuckin' bastard's deid!
Haw Maw, um just oan parole,
An noo I'm headin back tae Barlineeeee . . .

Haw Maw, ooh oohooh ooh,
Never meant tae steal yer purse,
But if I'm no fu' o' smack this time the morra'.
Carry oot, carry oot!
An we'll go oot oan the batter!

Too late, the bailiff's here,
Sends shivers doon ma spine,
Gubbed 10 jellies just in time.
Goodbye all ma muckers, I've got tae go,
Got tae go and rip some wank fae up the scheme.

Haw Maw, ooh oohooh ooh
I'm a jakey bam, I sometimes think I've never
been washed at all.
I see a little silhouetto of a bam,
Adidas! Adidas! Can ye get us a kergo?

Thunderbird, White Lightning,
very very frightning to me!
Twenty Mayfair,
Twenty Mayfair,
Twenty Mayfair and some skins,
Magnifico oh oh oh oh!
I'm just a fat boy, nae body loves me,
He's just a fat boy fae a fat family!
Spare us a pound fur a wee cup o tea?

Get tae fuck, skanky slob,
will ye get a job?
For fucksake, No! I will no' get a job! – Get a job!
For fucksake, I will no' get a job! – Get a job! For
fucksake, Will you get a job? – Get a job!

Will no' get a job, get a job!
Will no' get a job, get a job! No, no, no, no, no, no, . . .
Oh
gonorrhoea! gonorrhoea!
gonorrhoea and the clap!

Then doon the pub, has the barman put aside for me? For
me, for meeeee!?

So you 'hink you can slash me and pish in my eye?
So ye 'hink ye can chib me an' leave me to die?
Haw bawbag, can't dae this tae me bawbag!
Just wait till I'm oot, just wait till I'm right oot ma nut!

Fuck all really matters, Any one can see,
Fuck all really matters, fuck all really matters to me!

Any way the Clyde flows . . .

CHEER UP ALEX SMITH

Tune: 'Daydream Believer'

Oh If I had big strong wings,
Like the bluebird as she sings
If I had the arse of a crow
I would fly high in the sky
I would fly over Tannadice
And shite on the bastards below

Chorus
Cheer up Alex Smith oh what can it mean
to a sad Arab bastard
with a shite football team
(repeat)

Now I am a true Dee
and I think its plain to see
I am as happy as can be
But I know that I am right
when I say United's shite
And there is only one team in Dundee

Chorus (repeat)

Now through the good times and the bad
Through the happy and the sad
I will follow Dee through thick and thin
I will walk that million miles
To see that class Latino style
And I will always be a Dee

Chorus (repeat)

DUNDEE UNITED

FOUNDED: 1909
NICKNAME: THE ARABS, THOUGH THE WEE RED
BOOK SAYS IT IS THE TERRORS - HAVEN'T HEARD
THAT ONE IN A WHILE
BIGGEST WIN: 14-0 (NITHSDALE 1931)
BIGGEST LOSS: 1-12 (MOTHERWELL [YES!] 1954)
GROUND: TANNADICE PARK
FANZINES: THE FINAL HURDLE;
CAN I BRING MY DOG?

* * *

Love is in the Air
de de de de de de
Love is in the Air
de de de de de de
(etc)

United . . . Dundee United
I can't help falling in love with you
United . . . Dundee United
I can't help falling in love with you

This seems to have started in Dundee, for singing to Glasgow fans, widely regarded as thieves. It refers to High Street shoe shops only displaying one shoe of a pair, which is what the fans then allegedly steal.

Tune: 'Blue Moon'

One shoe, you've only got one shoe
You've only got one shoe
You've only got one shoe

Tune: 'Yellow Submarine'

In the town where I was born
Lived a man called Jerry Kerr
And he told me of his life
As United's manager
We all live in a tangerine machine
A tangerine machine
A tangerine machine
We all live in a tangerine machine
A tangerine machine
A tangerine machine

Homophiles rather than homophobes at United, it would appear.

Tune: 'Camptown Races'

Who's that boy with the golden hair
Andy Andy
Who's that boy with the golden hair
Andy Andy Gray
Andy Andy Gray
Andy Andy Gray
Who's that boy with the golden hair
Andy Andy Gray

Here's a plea:

Tune: 'Cecilia'

Oh United
I'm down on my knees
I'm begging you please
Score a goal

And a firm belief:

We'll score again
Don't know where

Don't know when
But I know we'll score again some sunny day

There has been a more significant massacre of the innocents since this particular September 11th event below.

THE DENS PARK MASSACRE OF '65

Get down on your knees and pray
It's the anniversary
Of the Dens Park massacre of '65 (65!)
It's the day we won't forget
And the Dundee will regret
It's the day we gave them 1 2 3 4 5!
It was the 11th of September
A day we all remember
Finn Dossing was at centre and scored three
Lennart Wing from the spot
And Gillespie with a shot
A shot that Ally Packy didn't see

*

Ivan Golac's magic, he wears a magic hat
He punched the bluenose in the puss
And now he's on his back
Ohhhhh Ivan Golac's magic . . .

No nay never
No nay never no more
Shall United be beaten
No never no more

HELLO HELLO

Hello hello, how do you do?
We fucked the boys in royal blue,
We fucked the boys in Aberdeen,
We are the boys in tangerine.

OLOFSSON

We have a forward his name is Olofsson
He only scores goals now and again
And again and again and again and again
His name is Olofsson!

UNITED BOYS

Hello! Hello! We are United boys
Hello! Hello! You'll tell us by our noise
We're up to our knees in Derry boys
Surrender or you'll die
For we are United boys

*

Let's all laugh at Dundee
Let's all laugh at Dundee
Haha ha ha, haha ha ha

DUNFERMLINE

FOUNDED: 1885
NICKNAME: THE PARS
BIGGEST WIN: 11-2 (STENHOUSEMUIR 1930)
BIGGEST LOSS: 0-10 (DUNDEE 1947)
GROUND: EAST END PARK

*   *   *

Chris Sutton's accusation that the Pars laid down to Rangers did not go down at all well in Dunfermline circles. Here's a ditty about it from a Pars fan called Kenny:

The Tims are coming to Fife today
They'd better come in disguise
The Tims are coming to Fife today
They're sure of a big surprise

For every Par that ever there was
Will be at East End for certain because
Today's the day we tell Big Chris
He's a wanker

And another:

Sutton's mutton dressed as lamb
The toys came oot the pram
The day he knew he'd won fuck all

Thompson bombed one ower the bar
And Sutton blamed the Pars
And we werenae even there

Had a great time in Seville
And won precisely . . . nil

The same as in Inverness
And at 5 o'clock the Pars and Sammy
Are going home to bed
But we don't lie down to Teddy Bears

And yet another:

His name was Sutton,
He was a wanker,
Paranoid beyond belief, words just can't describe his grief,
When Celtic blew it, away to Killie,
He claimed Dunfermline took a dive, while the Huns
scored more than five,
He thought "It's all a fix", "Coz no-one likes the 'tic",

Of course it's all a load of bollocks –
Sutton's just a prick . . .
In the East end, East end of Glasgow, where there's no
cups but plenty of arseholes,
In the East end, East end of Glaaaaaaaasssgooooooow,
they'll moan and they'll bore ya with much paranoia in
the East end . . .
They won fuck all . . .

A NEW HERO

He doesn't come from Holland,
He doesn't come from Spain
He comes from Lithuania
And Skerla is his name

You are my Skerla, my Andrei Skerla
You make me happy when skies are grey
We'd have Maldini but he's too greasy
Please don't take my Skerla away

Na na na nana nana
Nana na na Skerlaaaaaaa

And an old one:

Tune: 'Cumbaya'

Hamish French ma lord, Hamish French

Tune: (Blur) 'Country House'

Oh, you live in a slum, a very big slum
through in Falkirk
You're a jakey wee bas, and you take it up the ass
through in Falkirk
Oh you've never had a wash, and you think the tramps
are posh through in Falkirk
And you're gonna shag yer mum when you get back to
your slum through in Falkirk . . .

MAN! I FEEL LIKE A HOOLIE

The best thing about being a Hoolie
Is everybody gets a kickin' in the goolies

Oh oh oh we're totally mental, we'll never be gentle
And we're as hard as fuck uh-oh-oh-oh

Coz we are the hoolies and we're fuckin' nails
Man! I feel like a hoolie

YOU ARE MY HOOLIE

You are my hoolie, my only hoolie,
You make me happy, when skies are grey,
You're fucking mental, you're never gentle,
Please don't take my hoolie away.

WHEN YOU HEAR THE NOISE

We'll be comin', we'll be comin',
We'll be coming doon the road,
When you hear the noise of the East End Hoolie boys,
We'll be comin' doon the road . . .

WE'RE VERY VERY MENTAL

Tune: The Bran Flakes advert

Would you like your head kicked in?
Would you like your puss punched?
Would you like a stot in the gob?
Ask the Pars supporters,
That's a different matter,
They'll all respond . . .

We're mental, mental, very, very, mental!
We're very mental!

PARS ARE NUMBER ONE

Tune: 'Que Sera Sera'

When I was just a little boy,
I asked my mother 'What will I be?,
Will I be Falkirk? Will I be Pars?',
Here's what she said to me,
'Wash your mouth out son,
And get your father's gun,
And shoot all the Falkirk scum,
Pars are number 1'

DUNFERMLINE SOCCER HOOLIGANS

<u>Tune: 'You're Going Home
In a West Fife Ambulance'</u>

We're Dun-fer-mline So-ccer Hoo-ligans

A guy called staymental got in touch with me about the above hoolie songs, which were apparently written as a joke, but with his permission, I've decided to leave them in.

He gave me the following two as well.

<u>Tune: 'The Great Escape'</u>

*We are the loyal, Dunfermiline loyal,
Fuck Falkirk and George O'Boyle . . .*

And he says: "Digging into the past a wee bit, my all time favourite (although it has hee-haw to do with football, let alone the Pars) is:

*It was a nice day, I went for a swim,
I was impressed by the size of her quim,
And I bet you a dollar it was the size of a horse's collar,
Coz we are the East End Boys.*

EAST FIFE

FOUNDED: 1903
NICKNAME: THE FIFERS; THE METHIL MILAN
BIGGEST WIN: 13-2 (EDINBURGH CITY 1937)
BIGGEST LOSS: 0-9 (HEARTS 1957)
GROUND: NEW BAYVIEW PARK
FANZINE: AWAY FROM THE NUMBERS

* * *

Their best song is the one they sing for Cowdenbeath. It is already quoted on the Cowdenbeath page but it is worth repeating. It was written by Mike McColl, editor of the above fanzine, and in March 2002 it was voted the best fan song ever.

Tune: 'The Addams Family'

They're sleekit and they're smelly,
They're fae up near Lochgelly,
They've never seen a telly,
The Cowden family.

This is followed by a sort of sideways shuffle dance step while going: 'Duh-du-der-uh'.

> *The girls have got moustaches,*
> *They've all got nasty rashes,*
> *And nae c*** ever waashes,*
> *The Cowden Family.*

Chorus

A variation of 'It's Just One of Those Songs' and on an old lovelorn theme. If you can't get a woman, get a team.

> *Oh we're the boys on the social*
> *The boys on the dole*
> *We're so fucking ugly*
> *We can't get our hole*
> *But we all go mental*
> *When we score a goal*
> *Oh the Bayview Boys are in town,*
> *na na na*
> *na na na na na*
> *na na na na na*
> *ooh!*

According to Mike, they also sing:

No soap in Cowden,
Oh, there is no soap in Cowden
No soap in Co-owden
Oh, there is no soap in Cowden

To the tune of 'Juantanamera'. The fanzine produced t-shirts bearing this slogan during the early 90's. He also says, and I copy him precisely from his email:

'There was also a non football song that we sang all the time to the proper words and in full! It was 'The Lions Sleep Tonight'! The fanzine did a special video cam of one of our away games to Berwick for Sky Sports one year and our rendition of that took pride and place!'

And another regional variation on a theme. The original Bayview is gone, but the spirit lives:

Away the lads, you should have seen us coming
We're only here to drink your beer
and shag your fucking women
All the lads and lasses
Smiles upon their faces
Walking along the Wellesley Road
To see the Bayview aces

And finally, according to Mike: 'This is probably the most popular East Fife song after *The Cowden Family*':

I love a lassie
A bonny bonny lassie
She's as tight as the paper on the wall
She's got legs like a spider
I'd love to fucking ride her
Mary from Methilhill
Two, three, four
(repeat)

EAST STIRLINGSHIRE

FOUNDED: 1881
NICKNAME: THE SHIRE
BIGGEST WIN: 11-2 (VALE OF BANNOCK 1888)
BIGGEST LOSS: 1-12 (DUNDEE UNITED 1936)
GROUND: FIRS PARK

* * *

It is unclear whether it is the home or away team which the Shire fans are singing about:

You're no very good
You're no very good
You're no very
You're no very
You're no very good

In fact you fucking stink
In fact you fucking stink
In fact in fact
In fact in fact
In fact you fucking stink

ELGIN CITY

Founded: 1893
Nickname: The City
Biggest win: 18-1 (Brora Rangers 1960)
Biggest loss: 1-14 (Hearts 1939)
Ground: Borough Briggs

*   *   *

I can't find an Elgin song that no-one else sings. I'm sure that Elgin has produced its share of poets, dreamers etc, it's just that none of them go to the football.

FALKIRK

FOUNDED: 1876
NICKNAME: THE BAIRNS
BIGGEST WIN: 12-1 (LAURIESTON 1893)
BIGGEST LOSS: 1-11 (AIRDRIE 1951)
GROUND: BROCKVILLE PARK
FANZINES: ONE F IN FALKIRK, RUPERT'S ROAR

* * *

They sing this when the team runs out.

Na na na na
Na na na na
Way-a-ay
Falkirk Bai-rns

They do a lot of nah nas at Falkirk. Here are more:

Said Berty Mee to Bill Shankly
Have you heard of the North Bank Highbury
Shanks said no, I don't think so
But I've heard of the famous BROCKVILLE

Nah nah nah nah nah nah nah nah,
Nah nah nah nah nah nah nah
Nah nah nah nah nah nah nah
We are the Falkirk Bairns

Obsolete, but as tasteful as ever it was.

He's white he's blue
He shat in Simon's shoe
Ian McColl, Ian McColl

Another ex-god.

Hail, Hail Simon Stainrod,
He has great skills and looks like god
He is not a tim and he is not a prod
He is super Stainrod

Tune: 'Juantanamera'

One F in Falkirk
There's only one F in Falkirk
One F in Falkirk
There's only one F in Falkirk

Was the fanzine derived from the song or vice versa? As the egg said to the chicken while lying back and enjoying a fag after they'd been to bed: 'That settles that question'.

We're blue, We're white
We're fucking dynamite
Falkirk Bairns, Falkirk Bairns

*

You are my Falkirk
[OOH AHH]
my only Falkirk
[OOH AHH]
You make me happy, when skies are grey
You'll never know, who much I love you
And you'll never take my Falkirk away

*

We will follow Falkirk
Over land and sea
We will follow Falkirk
On to victory

FORFAR ATHLETIC

FOUNDED: 1873
NICKNAME: THE LOONS
BIGGEST WIN: 14-1 (LINDERTIS 1888)
BIGGEST LOSS: 2-12 (KINGS PARK 1930)
GROUND: STATION PARK
FANZINE: THE BRIDIE OF FRANKENSTEIN

* * *

It would appear that there is more than one F in Forfar. From scenes like these, Auld Scotia's grandeur springs. Exile must be a terrible thing, capable of warping the mind. Where do they find the *time?*

FORZA FORFAR
(THE LOONS AWAY)

As four-and-forty Forfar fans were faffin' aboot in Fife,
They fell in with a feck of East Fifers, then fell oot wi'
girt muckle strife,
The fruit of their foray was to meet – aye, just followin'
the fray –
Wi' supporters come from afar,
A squad of stuttering Stenhousemuir stalwarts,
Who'd stridden from the streets of Stranraer.

Now amongst the followers of Forfar were a brace of
bovver boys bold,
They had been at the bevvy, above all at the Heavy, and
couldnae tell Guinness from Gold.
'!!Forza Forfar!!' did they bellow at a poor Stenhousemuir
fellow, 'Doon wi' dozy denizens of Dens!
Dae ye dare tae deny that ye dawdle and dither when
ye're a' dribblin' for dowdy Dundee?
That it's due tae the Dewars and Double Diamonds to
boot, that ye doon wi' devil-may-care glee?'

Pride dented by this Dundee misidentification, the
stutterers of Stenhousemuir strove,

To set matters straight by stifling their stutters, stammering
'It's for St . . . St. Stenhousemuir that we rove'.

Interlude

Now before the staggered, stunned, stammering, stuttering, student Stenhousemuir supporters could stymie their dozy detractors' deviant Dundee misidensification, up came a crowd of cold, callow, cowed, cowled, Cowdenbeath choirboys keening, for the corners conceded to Cove Rangers in the Ma Cewan's Cup qualifiers.

Now almost as appropriately, and certainly every bit as alliteratively, an acrimonious 'andful of Accrington Stanley aficionados then alighted adroitly from an 'ansom cab at the apex of the avenue.

'Ayup,' they averred, 'Accrington 'aven't 'alf 'ad an awful 'ammerin' from 'amilton Academicals, and 'ad an admonition not bin 'anded out, albeit 'alf-'eartedly, to tha t 'alf-baked 'alf-back 'alf-wit 'alf way through the first 'alf o' the first 'alf, 'alf of Accrington 'd 've 'ad 'alf a mind to say, "Not 'alf to no 'alf measures!" – especially after that Alan Ball bookin'.'

In response to this, an army of 'amilton Academicals' activists articulated an aria with alacrity, adamantly alleging that 'The boy Ball butted the Accrington Stanley ballboy because the ballboy wouldnae boot the ball back tae the boy Ball; then, because the boy Ball butted the ballboy in the balls because the ballboy wouldnae boot the ball back tae the boy Ball, the ballboy began to bawl–all because the boy Ball butted the ballboy in the balls because the ballboy wouldnae boot the ball back tae the boy Ball' . . .

Just then a ragged rabble of Rangers rowdies ran rattlin' roarin' roond the roondaboot. As they leaped and lurched they relieved themselves of this lengthy ululation:

Awa' wi' a' Loons that linger and lurk
By oor goal line in limelight or mirk,
May they linger too long on the ball in the wet
And may the 'Gers aye lambast it in the back o' their net.

All began to bellow and boo when . . .

Stoically, the stung stirks of stout Stenhousemuir,
Started to state, in their stiff, stilted stutters,
That they were not devotees of dowdy Dundee,
But were strongly estranged from such duffers;

And though their stutters were stubborn,
and so were their stammers,
They staunchly stemmed them in time;
And looking sternly about them, they stood
sternum to sternum,
And succeeded in stating this rhyme . . .

THE SEWER OF STENHOUSEMUIR

As the sterling Stirling stalwarts stood in the stand at
Stenhousemuir,
A stealthy stench did seep without stint frae the stinking
Stenhouse sewer;
Of the fifty faithful full forty-five fled frae the fumes and
fxxxed off fast,
While the feisty five found the foul fumes fine and
fulminated as the fleers fled past:
'Stop the stampede and stay still in the stands, as we stick
it tae Stenhousemuir!
If a few feeble fumes force you fuxxxers tae flee, what d'
ye flock tae the fitba' fuir?'

and the authors conclude . . .

Unfortunately for all who live for the love of
alliterative literature, immediately after this brief

ootburst the stunned, staggered, staggering, struggling, stream of stern, strong-striding, stalwart, student, Stenhousemuir supporters were again stricken with an attack of the stutters – to such a degree that the final fate of the flee-ers from the Sewer of Stenhousemuir must remain for ever hidden from us four feckless, faithful but forlorn Forfar fitba' fans frettin' far frae Forfar.

!!!FORZA FORFAR!!!

Enough said, really, or should that be surreally? I'll have a pint of whatever it is they are drinking.

GRETNA

FOUNDED: 1946
NICKNAME: THE BLACK & WHITES,
AKA THE KINGS OF THE BORDER
GROUND: RAYDALE PARK

* * *

Gretna's Commercial Director, Steve Barker, tells me that they haven't been in the Scottish League long enough to learn to hate anyone properly yet, and that pro-Gretna songs have been slow in emerging. They'll learn.

HAMILTON ACCIES

FOUNDED: 1874
NICKNAME: THE ACCIES
BIGGEST WIN: 11-1 (CHRYSTON 1885)
BIGGEST LOSS: 1-11 (HIBS 1965)
GROUND: NEW DOUGLAS PARK
FANZINE: HASH

* * *

The Accies don't have their troubles to seek, not the least of which is that they don't seem to have any songs of their own.

HEART OF MIDLOTHIAN

FOUNDED: 1874
NICKNAME: THE JAM TARTS
BIGGEST WIN: 21-0 (ANCHOR 1880)
BIGGEST LOSS: 1-8 (VALE OF LEVEN 1888)
GROUND: TYNECASTLE PARK
FANZINES: ALWAYS THE BRIDESMAID,
NO IDLE TALK, BIG ON TYNIE

* * *

The classic:

H.. E.. A.. R.. T.. S

Away up in Gorgie at Tynecastle Park
There's a wee fitba' team that will aye make its mark
They've won all the honours in footballing arts
And there's nae other team to compare with the Hearts

Chorus
H.. E.. A.. R.. T.. S
If you cannae spell it then here's what it says

Hearts, Hearts, glorious Hearts
It's down at Tynecastle they bide
The talk of the toon are the boys in maroon
And Auld Reekie supports them with pride

This is my story, this is my song
Follow the Hearts and you can't go wrong
Oh some say that Celtic and Rangers are grand
But the boys in maroon are the best in the land

We've won the League flag and we've won
the League Cup
Though we sometimes go down we can aye go back up
Our forwards can score and it's no idle talk
Our defence is as strong as the auld castle rock

National caps we can always supply
Like Massey and Walker and Bauld and Mackay
If I had the time I could name dozens more
Who've helped in producing the auld Hampden roar

And a new version from Big Dave J:

H E A R T S
if you cannae spell it then here's whit it says
Hearts Hearts Glorious Hearts

It's With the Hibees they share
Their ground is half Green and one half Maroon
Wi that mix o' colour Laura Ashley would swoon

This is my story this is my song
fitba in Straiton cannae be wrong
Multiplex, Currys and bowling will thrive
In Witherspoons pubs the fans will imbibe

Said Petire to Pieman "you've got a point Chris
the Hibernian funds are somewhat amiss
we can build the new groond in my mate's back garden
Tom's just aff the bypass at sunny Straiton"

HEARTS

If you cannae spell it then here's what it says
Hearts and Hibs what have you done?
ER and Tynie have gone
Six Score years o' tradition gone doon the pan
Whilst Pieman and Petire now work on their tans!

This is my story this is my song!
Buy flats in Auld Reekie – you can't go wrong
Estate agents will be happy to show you aroond
The executive flats that were once hallowed groond.

So noo we're in Straiton wi' oor Hibee mates
We've buried the hatchet and all oor pet hates
Oor finances no longer make the bank squirm
Perhaps there's the cash to beat the Old Firm

HEARTS

If you cannae spell it then here's what it says
Hearts and Hibs what will the world think
Mix green and maroon and you get a foul pink
Will Petire and Pieman get royally knighted
for taking the first steps to a Rekkie United??

This is my story this is my song!
Fitba in Straiton feels a bit wrong
Like everything else in oor culture today
If ye cannae 'Drive Thru' then throw it away!!

WE'RE GOING TO EUROPE

Tune: 'My Way'

And now, the end is near
We've followed Hearts, from Perth to Paisley
We've travelled far, by bus and car

And other times, we've went by railway
We've been, to Aberdeen
We hate the Hibs, they make us spew up
So make a noise you Gorgie Boys
We're going to Europe
To see, HMFC
We'll even dig, the Channel Tunnel
When we're afloat, on some big boat
We'll tie our scarves, around the funnel
We have no cares, for other players
Like Rossi, Boniek or Tardelli
When we're overseas, the Hibs will be
In Portobelly

We all can laugh, at Hibs
When we play Chelsea, Metz or Inter
They'll be up at Dundee
And relegated by mid winter
While we go, marching on
And show the Huns, the way to do it
They lost again, while we had slain
The might of Europe

<u>(Same tune)</u>

We all can laugh at Hibs
When we play Chelsea, Metz or Inter
They'll travel far, to see Stranraer
and visit Airdrie in the winter
While Hearts, go marching on
and show the Hibs the way to do it
they lost at Ayr, and we don't care
we're going to Europe
The days, not far away
when we will reach the heights of glory
We'll follow Hearts through foreign parts
and Gorgie boys will tell the story
How we scored three, at Napoli
took care of Bierhoff and Vieri
when we're overseas
the Hibs will watch us on the telly

MARCHIN' THRU GORGIE

Chorus
Hurrah, hurrah, we are the Gorgie boys
Hurrah, hurrah, we make a lot of noise
On Saturdays you'll hear us sing
Tynecastle to Dalry
When we go marchin' thru' Gorgie

Walking down the Gorgie Road on a Saturday
Doon to old Tynecastle where the gallant Hearts do play
We've followed them a hundred years
And will a hundred mair
Still we go marchin' thru Gorgie

Chorus

There's Kenny Garland in the goal keepin oot the ba'
Gallagher and Jefferies,
and there's no a better twa
Bobby Prentice on the wing,
while Fordie knocks them in
That's what we see at Tynecastle

Chorus
but last line
W-h-e-n w-e g-o m-a-rchin th-r-u G-o-r-g-i-e.

WHEN THE HEARTS GO MARCHING IN

Oh when the Hearts, go marching in
Oh when the Hearts, go marching in
I wanna be in that number
When the Hearts go marching in

A MILLION MILES

Oooooooh Jaaam Tarts, Jaaam Tarts
I'd walk a million miles
for one of your goals,
Oh Jaaam Tarts

(there is a version which goes
I'd kick a million holes)

*

We love you Jam Tarts, oh yes we do
We love you Jam Tarts, oh yes we do
We Love you Jam Tarts we do,
Oh Jam Tarts we love you

IN DUBLIN'S FAIR CITY

In Dublin's fair City
where the girls are so pretty
I first set my eyes on sweet Molly Malone
As she wheeled her wheelbarrow
Through streets broad and narrow
Singing (clap clap clap clap clap clap
clap clap clap) JAM TARTS

HELLO HELLO

Hello, Hello we are the Gorgie boys
Hello, Hello you'll know us by our noise
We're up to our knees in Hibee blood
Surrender or you'll die
For we are the Gorgie bovver boys

HEY JUDE

(to be accompanied by lots of scarf waving)

Hey Jude, don't make it bad
take a sad song and make it better
remember to let her into your heart
then you can start
to make it better . . . better . . . better . . . better . . .
na na na na-na-na-na, na-na-na-na Jam Tarts
na na na na-na-na-na, na-na-na-na Jam Tarts

FOREVER AND EVER,
WE'LL FOLLOW THE BOYS

Forever and ever, we'll follow the boys
The Edinburgh Jam Tarts, The Gorgie Boys
For we will be mastered, by no Hibby bastard
We'll keep the Hearts flag flying high
So bring on the Hibs, the Celts, the Rangers
Bring on the Spaniards by the score
Barcelona, Real Madrid
WE WILL MAKE A GALLANT BID
For we're out to show the world
what we can do

THE SILVERY MOON

By the light, (6 claps)
of the silvery moon (6 claps)
We're the talk of the toun (6 claps)
We're the boys in maro-o-n
Repeat

Tune: 'It's Just One of those Songs'

His name is Drew Busby the talk of the north
He comes from Tynecastle just over the Forth
He drinks all your whiskyand Newcastle Brown
The Gorgie Boys are in town – na na na na
na na na na na
The Gorgie boys are in town.

Another version:

Lock all your windows and bolt all your doors
Hide all your daughters and lie on the floors
Stash all your whisky and Newcastle Brown
The Gorgie Boys are in town –

na na na na na na na na
The Gorgie boys are in town

Or another version:

They've won all the honours in snooker and darts
There's no other team to compare with the Hearts
We've fucked the Kilmarnock and Dumbarton too
And now were gonna fuck you na na na na . . .

<u>Tune: 'Guide me O thy Great Jehovah'</u>

Heart of Midlothian, Fuck off Hibernian
We'll support you evermore
Heart of Midlothian, Fuck off Hibernian
We'll support you evermore
We'll support you
We'll support you
We'll support you evermore
We'll support you evermore

<u>Tune: 'She'll be Coming Round the Mountain'</u>

If you're proud to be a Jamboclap your hands
If you're proud to be a Jamboclap your hands

if you're proud to be a Jambo proud to be a Jambo
proud to be a Jambo clap your hands
(loud sustained applause)

Tune: <u>'We Are the Champions'</u>

We are the Jam Tarts my friend
And we'll keep on fighting to the end
We are the Jam Tarts, We are the Jam Tarts
No time for Hibees, for we Are the Jam Tarts

Tune: <u>'I Will Survive'</u>

At first I was afraid, I was petrified
Kept thinking Hibs were gonna beat
my famous Jambo side
But then I spent so many hours
drinking lager in a pub And then I knew
Hearts were the greatest football club
Go on now go, Go Jambos go
put the ball into the net
and tell the Hibbys where to go
They couldn't beat us if they played the game all night
That's cos Hibs are dirty, rotten,
smelly first division SHITE

GORGIE BOOT BOYS

Said a bow-legged chicken to a knock-kneed hen
I haven't been so happy since I don't know when
I walk with a wiggle and I wiggle when I walk
we are the Gorgie boot boys
with a na na na na na n na na na na na na,
na na na na na na na –
we are the Gorgie boot boys

GLORY GLORY GLORY

Glory Glory Glory, listen to the band
we're the Embra Jam Tarts
best team in the land

THE NORTHERN LIGHTS
OF OLD ABERDEEN

The northern lights of old Aberdeen
mean sweet fuck all to me
The northern lights of Aberdeen
mean sweet fuck all to me
I've been a Hearts fan all of my life
And many a sight I've seen
but the northern lights of Aberdeen
mean sweet fuck all to me!

*

Show them the way to go home
They're tired and they want to go to bed
For they're only half a football team
and the other half is dead

*

Can you hear the Hearts fans sing – yo-o yo-o
Can you hear the Hearts fans sing – yo-o yo-o
can you hear the Hearts fans sing
You're gonna get your heads kicked in- yo-o-o-o-o-o-o
Can you hear the Hibs fans sing – no-o no-o
Can you hear the Hibs fans sing – no-o no-o

Can you hear the Hibs fans sing
I can't hear a fucking thing – yo-o-o-o-o

*

<u>Tune: 'Polly Wolly Doodle'</u>

Oh it's all gone quiet over there
Oh it's all gone quiet over there
Oh it's all gone quiet, all gone quiet,
all gone quiet over there
(or alternatively)
Can you sing a wee bit louder over there
Can you sing a wee bit louder over there
Can you sing a wee bit louder,
sing a wee bit louder
sing a wee bit louder over there –
if you can – CAN YOU FUCK!

DRINK, DRINK

<u>Tune: 'Lord of the Dance'</u>

Drink, drink, wherever you may be,
We are the drunk and disorderly,
but we don't give a shit,
and we don't give a fuck,
we came home with the Scottish Cup!

*

Away in a manger, no crib for a bed,
the little Lord Jesus stood up and he said . . .
WE HATE HIBEES AND WE HATE HIBEES,
WE HATE HIBEES AND WE HATE HIBEES, WE
ARE THE HIBEE HATERS

This is a classic from the 70s.

Tune: 'Teddy Bears Picnic'

If you go down to the woods today
you're sure of a big surprise
if you go down to the woods today
you'll never believe your eyes
For Jeremy the Sugar Puff bear
is putting on braces and cropping his hair
and now he's off to join the Gorgie boot boys

Tune: 'Gin Gan Goolie'

Hit him on the head, hit him on the head
Hit him on the head with a baseball bat
– Oh yeah, oh yeah
See how he goes, see how he goes
See how he goes with a broken nose
– Oh yeah, oh yeah

WE'RE THE BEST BEHAVED
SUPPORTERS IN THE LAND

Tune: 'She'll be Coming Round the Mountain'

The first verse is sung in a high pitched voice, the second in a very deep v. tough guy voice. Try it, it's fun.

We're the best behaved supporters in the land
We're the best behaved supporters in the land
We're the best behaved supporters,
best behaved supporters
best behaved supporters in the land
(when we win).

We're a right shower of bastards when we lose (or draw)
We're a right shower of bastards when we lose (or draw)
We're a right shower of bastards,
right shower of bastards
right shower of bastards when we lose (or draw).

<u>Tune: 'Hi Lo Silver Lining'</u>

You're everywhere and nowhere, Alan,
That's where you are!
When Sandy Clarke and Ian Jardine,
Fire just below the bar!
But the favourite is the wee man, Robbo,
As he knocks one home,
But you've even missed a looping header . . .
Nodded in by JIMMY BONE !
And it's
High, low, balls fly past him,
And it's Alan Rough, (Poor Alan)
Each time Hearts stuff the Hibees,
And he's had enough,
(Oh yes, it's obvious).
To go and see the Edinburgh Derby,
It's great if you're a Jam Tarts fan,
And afterwards the celebrations,
As only Hearts fans can,
For comedy there's Fulton and Hunter,
Nine other jokers too,
At half time there's the entertainment,
From the monkeys out of Edin-burgh Zoooooo,
and it's,
High, low, balls fly past him,
And it's Alan Rough, (Poor Alan)

Each time Hearts stuff the Hibees,
And he's had enough, (Oh yes, it's obvious)

Tune: 'Perfect Day'

Just a perfect day, Bovril at Tynecastle Park
and then later when it gets dark
Mickey scores
Just a perfect day
Put Celtic fans in the zoo
And later goal number two – and then home
Oh it's such a perfect day
I'm so glad I support you
Oh such a perfect day
You just keep me hanging on
You just keep me hanging on
Just a perfect day
Problems are left alone
Hibs are down on their own
It's such fun!
Just a perfect day
You made me forget myself
I thought I was someone else – we'd scored 2
Oh it's such a perfect day, I'm so glad I support you
Oh such a perfect day

You just keep me hanging on
You just keep me hanging on

*

Jam Tarts here, Jam Tarts there
Jam Tarts every fucking where
Na na na na na na na na na

*

They dive, they fall,
Their goalposts are too small,
Majorca, Majorca.

MY OLD MAN'S A HEARTS FAN

Tune: 'My Old Man's a Dustman'

Kruschev came to Britain, 2nd time he'd been
He met Sir Winston Churchill, he even met the Queen
And when his time was over he was to be recalled
He said 'I cannae go now 'cos I've not met Willie Bauld'
Oh my old man's a Hearts fan, he wears a Hearts fans hat
He hates the fucking Hibees, now what do you
think of that?

*

Ay ay ay ay, Cruikshank is better then Yashin
Ernie is better than Eusebio
And the Hibees are in for a bashing

CROWN WILLIE BAULD
THE KING OF SCOTLAND

Tune: 'Tramp, Tramp, Tramp'

There is a team in Scotland, their colours are maroon
they've got the finest centrethe world has ever known
you talk about your Reilly's your Ormonds and them all
but you want to hear the crowd roar when
King Willie gets the ball.
Crown Willie Bauld the king of Scotland
Crown Willie Bauld the king of Scotland
Crown Willie Bauld the king of Scotland
(and Gordon Smith the Queen)

Tune: 'On Top of Old Smokey'

There's a team at Tynecastle
They play in maroon
They have a young centre in a class of his own
Now come all ye faithful

come listen to me
I'll tell you a story, that will fill you with glee
The Hibs they will wither
the Rangers will die
And down at Tynecastle, the league flag will fly
We'll try for the Scottish
the League Cup too
With Bauld in the centre, we'll win them all

You have to be at least two up and playing well to sing this:

So fucking easy,
oh this is so fucking easy,
so fucking easy,
oh this is so fucking easy.
(A variation is to sing boring.)

We're going up, you're going down,
We're gonna wreck your fucking town.
We're going to rape, we're going to pillage,
We're gonna wreck your fucking village.
We'll see you all outside,
We'll see you all outside
We'll see you all, we'll see you all outside.

Another one for The Sheep Shaggers. To the 'Hello Hello' tune, sing the whole song singing *baa*.

*

Who put the ball in the Hibees net,
Robbo, Robbo,
Who put the ball in the Hibees net,
Johnny Robertson,
Johnny Robertson (ONCE),
Johnny Robertson (TWICE),
Who put the ball in the Hibees net,
Johnny Robertson.

Sung after being relegated in 1976/77 to the Hibs fans, to the tune 'Remember You're a Womble':

We'll be back to get you, we'll be back to get you

Tune: 'You are my Sunshine'

You are my Jackson, my Darren Jackson
You make me happy when skies are grey
You'll never know just how much I love you
Please don't take my Jackson away!

H.. E.. A.. R.. T.. S

Away up in Gorgie at Tynecastle Park
There's a wee fitba' team that will aye make its mark
They've won all the honours in footballing arts
And there's nae other team to compare with the Hearts

Chorus
H.. E.. A.. R.. T.. S
If you cannae spell it then here's what it says
Hearts, Hearts, glorious Hearts
It's down at Tynecastle they bide
The talk of the toon are the boys in maroon
And Auld Reekie supports them with pride

This is my story, this is my song
Follow the Hearts and you can't go wrong
Oh some say that Celtic and Rangers are grand
But the boys in maroon are the best in the land
We've won the League flag and we've won
the League Cup
Though we sometimes go down we can aye go back up

Chorus

Our forwards can score and it's no idle talk
Our defence is as strong as the auld castle rock

National caps we can always supply
Like Massey and Walker and Bauld and Mackay
If I had the time I could name dozens more
Who've helped in producing the auld Hampden roar

Chorus

*

I wanna be a Hearts supporter
I'm gonna dye ma hair maroon
I'm gonna be a Hearts supporter
I wanna look like John Colquhoun

Tune: 'Big Ben'

Juanjo, Juanjo – Juanjo Juanjo
You're so shite it's unbelievable . . .

To any team when they are relegated:

*We'll meet again, don't know where
Don't know when, but I know we'll meet again
Some sunny day*

And some assorted jibes and threats:

*You're going to get
What the fucking Hibees got*

You're going home in a fucking ambulance

What's it like to see a crowd . . .

*Come in a taxi,
you must have come in a taxi . . .*

Score in a brothel, you couldn't score in a brothel . . .

What a waste of money . . .

What a load of rubbish!

Come and have a go with the Gorgie aggro

Come and have a go if you think you're hard enough

Get intae them (we're over here)

If you're all going to . . . clap your hands. . . .

Celtic Celtic, get tae fuck, Celtic get tae fuck
(Any team – or referee – will do)

We can see you sneaking out
We can see you sneaking out

What a shitey home support
What a shitey home support

And now a word for the snappers and the cameramen:

Wrong fucking end
You're at the wrong fucking end

*

Hello Hello we are the Gorgie Boys
Hello Hello you'll know us by our noise
We are all fucking starving
And we will tell you why
'Cos Paul Gascoigne's eaten all the pies!

*

Hamish is a poofy name, poofy name
Hamish is a poofy name, he's a poofy bastard

He's fat, he's round
His team is going down
Jimmy Bone, Jimmy Bone!
He's fat, he's round
He bounces on the ground
Jimmy Bone, Jimmy Bone!

Any player, but Davie Dodds definitely started it off:

So fucking ugly, oh you are so fucking ugly

And now a word for the Managing Director:

Who sold all the players,
Who sold all the players,
You fat bastard,
You fat bastard,
You sold all the players.

HARPER'S A BARREL,
HARPER'S A BARREL OF SHITE

Tune: 'Roll Out the Joe Harper', sorry, 'the Barrel'

Joe Harper's as fat as he's funny
Hibs spent a barrel of money
He wears green and white
He's just a wee shite bye bye Joey
The Hibees have spent a lot of money
Joe Harpers fat and he's funny
Built like a tank,
Plays like a wank
Wee fat Joe

*

Jingle bells Jingle Bells
Jingle all the way
Oh what fun it is to fuck
The Hibs on New Years day

*

Cheer up Jim Duffy, Oh what can it be
To a sad Hibee bastard,
And a shite football team

Repeat until your ears bleed.

Tune: 'Nelly the Elephant'

Robbo the greatest he scored the goal
That beat the fucking Hibees
And off he went with a trumpety trump
Trump trump trump

Tune: 'Singing the Blues'

I never felt more like sinking the booze
When Robbo scores and the Hibees lose
Oh Robbo, you've got me sinking the booze

In your Easter Road slums
In your Easter Road slums
You rake in the buckets for something to eat
You find a dead rat and you think its a treat
In your Easter Road slums

Tune: 'Una Paloma Blanca'
The white dove of peace. See irony. See Hearts fans.

We hate the fuckin Hibees
We hate them all of the day
We hate the fuckin Hibees
We chase all the bastards away
Oh ay ay ay etc.

Tune: 'Three Lions'

You're going down, you're going down, you're going
Hibs are going down, they're going down

Tune: 'Ten Green Bottles'

(But you guessed. Good for l-o-o-o-o-ng bus trips.)
Ten fucking Hibees sitting on the wall
Ten fucking Hibees sitting on the wall
Ten fucking Hibees sitting on the wall
And if one fucking Hibee should accidentally fall
There'll be nine fucking Hibees sitting on the wall

Tune: 'Good to be Back'

Happy New Year Happy New Year,
Hello, Hello,
Happy New Year, Happy New Year,
Hello, Hello.

If you hate the fucking Hibees clap your hands
If you hate the fucking Hibees clap your hands
If you hate the fucking Hibees
hate the fucking Hibees
hate the Fucking Hibees clap your hands

Normally, if we can bend the meaning of the word normally a bit, sung to loud applause at the end.

Tune: 'Go West'

Stand up if you hate Hibees,
Stand up if you hate Hibees,
Stand up if you hate Hibees,
Stand up if you hate Hibees.

Or:

Away, we fucking hate Hibees,
Away we fucking hate Hibees,
Away, we fucking hate Hibees,
Away we fucking hate Hibees.

Tune: 'My Bonny Lies Over the Ocean'

If I had the wings of a sparrow
and the dirty backside of a crow
I'd fly over Easter Road tomorrow
and shite on the bastards below, below
shite on, shite on, shite on the bastards below

Tune: 'Seasons in the Sun'

We had joy we had fun
we had Hibees on the run
but the fun didn't last
cos the bastards ran too fast

We threw sticks we threw stones
We broke all the bastards bones
But the fun didn't last
'Cos the bastards ran too fast

VALDEREE

Oh I love to go a-wandering,
Along the cliffs of Dover,
And if I see Hibees there,
I'll push the bastards over.

*

He's gay, he's bent, his arse is up for rent
Any player, any player

Sung whenever an opposition player is down:

Glory Glory what a hell of a way to die
Glory Glory what a hell of a way to die
Glory Glory what a hell of a way to die
To die a Hibee bastard
Relegation to the Hibees,
Relegation to the Hibees
Relegation to the Hibees
As the Hearts go marching on on on

Sung to the Who tune 'My Generation'

We all know you're going down
(talkin 'bout your relegation)
It's the best thing to happen in town
(talkin 'bout your relegation)
It's great to say goodbye and no one here is going to cry
talking 'bout your relegation
your relegation, your relegation, yeah!

And in true *Tiswas* style:

Easter Road . . . compost corner
Easter Road . . . compost corner

Another one to the Gary Glitter 'Hello Hello' riff:

Green and white shite,green and white shite . . .
hello hello

A nice wee carol tune:

Can you hear the Hearts fans sing
The Hibees ran away
And Alex Miller and his muppet men
Got fucked on New Years Day

NO MORE HIBEES

Tune: 'No More Heroes'

No more Hibees anymore,
No more Hibees anymore,
We fuck the bastards by the score,
Whatever happened to all the Hibees . . . ?

There was a newspaper report that Hibs were starting
a gay fanzine. Petrol on a non-PC bonfire:

Jingle bells, jingle bells, jingle all the way
Hearts are heterosexual
And the Hibs are fucking gay

*

It's magic, you know
Hibees and females don't go
Send your females over here
Send your females over here
They've won the league cup and we don't give a fuck
Cos it's 98 QUEERS in a row

*

*He's gay, he's bent, his legs are heaven sent
Any player, any player*

*

*Stand up if you like pussy
Stand up if you like pussy*

*

*No poofs in Gorgie,
Oh there are no poofs in Gorgie*

*

*Hibs are gay, Hibs are gay, Hibs are gay
Hibs are gay, Hibs are gay, Hibs are gay etc*

*

And as for Alex McLeish:

*Cheer up ginger whinger oh what can it be
To a sad Hibby bastard and a gay football team
Cheer up Ginger Tosser oh what can it mean
To a sad Hibby bastard and some queer football queens*

Gay gay Frank Sauzee
Gay gay Frank Sauzee
Gay gay Frank Sauzee he is very . . . gay

Applies to any player whose name fits.

To the Robin Hood tune:

Anyone, Anyone takes it up the arse
Anyone, Anyone takes it up the arse
Get him in a taxi, he'll take it up the jacksie
Anyone, Anyone.

*

Glasgow Rangers, Glasgow Rangers
You're not fit to wear the sash
You're not fit to wear the sash

More Tims than Celtic
Oh you've got more Tims than Celtic
More Tims than Celtic
Oh you've got more Tims than Celtic

*

No soap in Glasgow
Oh there is no soap in Glasgow
No soap in Glasgow
Oh there is no soap in Glasgow

*

Sing in your chapels
You only sing in your chapels
Sing in your chapels
You only sing in your chapels

Tune: 'The Fields of Athenry'

Look at that sadshower of bigots from Glasgow
That only sing about Ireland
We don't need a Pope or a Queen
To sing about our footballing team
Only Celtic and Rangers are that sad
Hello Hello, how do you do?
We hate the boys in royal blue
We hate the orange and the green
So stuff the Pope and stuff the Queen.

*

The hills are alive with the sound of . . .
John Greig's a bastard

*

What's it like to have a wash?
What's it like to have a wash?

*

As I was slowly walking by Tynecastle Park one day
I stopped just for a moment to see the Jam Tarts play
Alone a man was standing I stopped and asked him why
He said 'We are the Gorgie boys surrender or you'll die'

Tune: 'The Sparrow Song'

He's only a poor little Hibby
His shirt was all tattered and torn
He started to sing, so I filled the twat in
And now he don't sing any more

*

Who's that man with the helmet on, Dixon, Dixon
Who's that man with the helmet on,

Dixon of Dock Green.
On the beat all day, on the wife all night
Who's that man with the helmet on,
Dixon of Dock Green

*

Who's your father, who's your father,
Who's your father referee?
You havnae got one, havnae got one,
You're a bastard, referee.

or

Who's the bastard in the black?
Who's the bastard in the black?

or

Who's the wanker in the black?
Who's the wanker in the black?

or, that well known instruction to a former TV programme:

Dallas, Dallas, get tae fuck. Dallas, get tae fuck.

Tune: 'Whistle While You Work'

Get it up you while yer young
Get it up you while yer young
Cause when yer old yer balls get cold
Get it up you while yer young

FOLLOW, FOLLOW

Follow, follow we will follow Jam Tarts
Anywhere, everywhere, we will follow on
Dundee, Hamilton, Partick or the Vatican
If they go to Dublin we will follow on

There's not a team like the Embra Jam Tarts
No not one, no not one
The Hibees know all about their troubles
We will fight till the day is won
There's not a team like the Embra Jam Tarts
No not one, no not one

I'M LOVING JAM TARTS INSTEAD

So when I'm lying in my bed thoughts of
Tynie in my head
Wishing everyone was dead
I'm loving Jam Tarts instead.
And through it all they have a new direction
A European connection
The Jambos sing their song
And win or fall wherever it may take me

I know that life won't break me
When I come to call
They won't forsake me
I'm loving Jam Tarts instead

Tune: 'You Are My Sunshine'

He's Colin Cameron, the Jambo's captain,
He made us happy, 16th of May,
He scored the spotkick,
That made the Huns sick,
Please don't take my Jam Tarts away.

He's Stephane Adam, monsieur not madame,
He made us happy, 16th of May,
Left Amaruso to play Subbuteo,
Please don't take my Jam Tarts away.

Tune: '500 Miles' by the Proclaimers

It has been 100 years and it will be 100 more
Till the Hibs will see the cup once more
And the Hearts fans the are laughing all the way
Ha Ha Ha Ha, Ha Ha Ha Ha etc

Tune: 'My Old Man's a Dustman'

We are Hearts supporters
We're Gorgie Boys for life
We hate the fucking Old Firm
And all that's north of Fife

But when we see a Hibeee
It has to end in tears
They haven't won the Scottish Cup
For a HUNDRED FUCKIN YEARS

Tune: 'She'll Be Coming Round the Mountain'

Have you ever seen the Hibees win the Cup
Have you ever seen the Hibees win the Cup
Have you ever seen the Hibees,
ever seen the Hibees
Ever seen the Hibees win the Cup
Have you fuck

Same tune:

If you want to go to heaven when you die
If you want to go to heaven when you die
You must wear a maroon bonnet
With fuck the Hibs upon it
If you want to go to heaven when you die

THE EUROPHANT SONG

OOoooooooohhhhhhhhh
Wee Mickey Cameron scored the goal
that left the Rangers trembling
And Hearts are off to a positive start
trump, trump trump.
The man in the sky was calling

from far far away
you'll win the cup and you'll sing like fuck
believe in me today!
OOoooooooooohhhhhhhhh
Stephane the Frenchman scored the goal
that left the Rangers with nothing
And Hearts fans all with a passionate voice
trump, trump trump.
The man in the sky was calling
from far far away
you'll win the cup and you'll sing like fuck
for ever and a day!
OOoooooooooohhhhhhhhh
Lockie and Fulton lifted the cup
and the fans went into raptures
And Robbo was there
with his hand on his heart
trump, trump trump.
The man in the sky is a Jambo
and this is all we'll say
we've won the cup and we're on the up
and the next stop is CALAIS!

HIBERNIAN

Founded: 1875
Nickname: The Hibees
Biggest win: 22-1 (42nd Highlanders 1881)
Biggest loss: 0-10 (Rangers 1896)
Ground: Easter Road
Fanzines: Mass Hibsteria,
Hibees Here Hibees There

* * *

We are Hibernian FC
We hate Jam Tarts and we hate Dundee
We will fight wherever we may be
'Cause we are the mental H F C

HAIL HAIL

Hail Hail the Hibs are here
All for goals and glory
All for goals and glory
Hail Hail the Hibs are here
All for goals and glory now
For it's a grand old team to play for
And it's a grand old team to say
That if you know your history
It's enough to make your heart go-oh-oh-oh
We don't care what the animals say
What the hell do we care
For all we know
Is there's going to be a show
And the Edinburgh Hibess will be there
(And the Edinburgh Jam Tarts will be there –
Selling the programmes)

IN YOUR GORGIE SLUMS

In your Gorgie slums
You rake in the bucket for something to eat
You find a dead rat and you think it's a treat
In your Gorgie slums

BYE BYE JAM TARTS

Jim O'Rourke thought he was set
When he put the ball in the Jam Tart's net
Bye Bye Jam Tarts

Alan Gordon running through
Coolly stroked in number two
Bye Bye Jam Tarts

Bobby Seith thought that he was only dreaming
When Arthur Duncan hammered number three in
Bye Bye Jam Tarts

The Hibees choir sang for more
Alex Cropley made it four
Bye Bye Jam Tarts

Hearts defenders on the skive
Arthur Duncan made it five
Bye Bye Jam Tarts

Don't know what happened with goal number six.

Eddie Turnbull was in heaven
When Alan Gordon knocked in number seven
Bye Bye Jam Tarts

WEEGIE SCUM SONG

As I was walking along the Copland Road
I met a total stranger
He said to me, are you going to see
The famous Glasgow Rangers

So I went along to Ibrox Park
Just to see the famous Glasgow Rangers
But the boys in blue, got fucked six two
By the Famous Edinburgh Hibees
N' NAH NAH NAH NAH NAH
NAH NAH NAH NAH . . .

HIBEES WE LOVE YOU

We hate Glasgow Rangers,
We hate Celtic too, they're shite,
We hate Heart of Midlothian,
But the Hibees we love you,
(altogether now)

THE HEARTS SONG

Hearts, Hearts glorious Hearts
It's down at Tynecastle they hide
The boys in maroon are the shite of the toon
And Auld Reekie supports Meadowbank

This is our story, this is our song
Follow the Jam Tarts and you're sure to go wrong
And some say the Rangers and Celtic are grand
But the boys in maroon are the shite of the land

Chorus
H-E-A-R-T-S
If you cannie spell it then here's what it says
Shite shite glorious shite
It's down at Tynecastle they hide

The boys in maroon are the shite of the toon
And Auld Reekie supports Meadowbank

This is our story, this is our song
McDonald and Jardine couldn't go wrong
Then suddenly Dundee are two up at Dens
And the boys from Tynecastle had blown it again

Chorus

This is our story, this is our song
Follow the Jam Tarts and you're sure to go wrong
They've won all the honours for Dominoes and Darts
There's no other team to compare with the Hearts

Chorus

WHO DO YOU THINK YOU ARE KIDDING?

Tune: 'Dads Army'

Who do you think you are kidding Mr Jefferies
If you think you're number one
We are the boys from the Leith San Siro
We are the boys who have fucked you seven zero

7 MORE THAN YOU

We scored one
We scored two
We scored seven more than you
Na na na na na na na na

7-0 SONG

We've played in South Morocco,
And we've played in the USA,
But the greatest game in history,
Was the game on New Year's Day,
7-0.

OOH TO BE A HIBEE

Ooh to
Ooh to be
Ooh to be a Hibee

INVERNESS
CALEDONIAN THISTLE

FOUNDED: 1995
NICKNAME: CALEY
BIGGEST WIN: 8-1 (ANNAN ATHLETIC 1998)
BIGGEST LOSS: 0-4 (QUEEN'S PARK 1937)
GROUND: CALEDONIAN STADIUM

* * *

Tune: 'Lord of the Dance'

Carefree wherever we may be
We are the famous ICT
Jambos 1 Caley Thistle 3
We are the famous ICT

They also do a very spirited version of:
We HATE Dundee and we HATE Dundee
We HATE Dundee and we HATE Dundee
We HATE Dundee and we HATE Dundee
We are the Dundee HATERS

. . . and a strange *Wizard of Oz* thing and 'Two Little Boys'. Go figure.

KILMARNOCK

FOUNDED: 1869
NICKNAME: KILLIE
BIGGEST WIN: 11-1 (PAISLEY ACADEMICAL'S 1930)
BIGGEST LOSS: 1-9 (CELTIC 1938)
GROUND: RUGBY PARK
FANZINE: HELP ME MAKE IT THROUGH THE NIGHT

* * *

God knows why, but they do sing this.

PAPER ROSES

*I realise the way your eyes deceive me, with tender looks
that I mistook for love,
So take away those flowers that you gave me, and send
the kind that you remind me of.
Paper roses, paper roses, oh how real those roses seem to me,
But they're only, imitation, like your imitation love for me.
I thought that you might be the perfect lover, you seemed
so full of sweetness at the start,
But like a big red rose that's made of paper, there isn't any
sweetness in your heart.*

Paper roses, paper roses, oh how real those roses seem to me,
But they're only, imitation, like your imitation love for me.

A peaen of praise for a stadium builder:

<u>Tune: You'll never guess!</u>

B*** the builder . . .
can he fix it?
B*** the builder . . .
can he fuck!!!

Gordon the gaffer
can he do it?
Gordon the gaffer
can he fuck!
B*** the builder . . .
can he fix it?
B*** the builder . . .
can he fuck!!!!!

Ayr United . . .
Ayr United . . .
have they ever won it?
Ayr United . . .
have they fuck!!!!!

B*** the builder . . .
can he fix it?
B*** the builder . . .
can he fuck!!!!!

Yet another version:

In yer Glasgow slums
In yer Glasgow slums
Ye pick up a rat and you think its a treat
Ye pick up a box cos you live in the street
In yer Glasgow slums!!

And for Glasgow teams only:

What's it like to steal a car?
What's it like to steal a car?
What's it like to?
What's it like to? . . .
What's it like to steal a car?

WHERE'S OOR TRACTORS?

Where's oor tractors?
Where's oor tractors?
Where's oor tractors?
Rogues and toerags.

Thieving bastards!
Thieving bastards!
Thieving bastards!
Rogues and toerags.

Tune: 'She'll be Coming Round the Mountain'

I will wear a Killie bonnet 'til I die, I will wear a Killie
bonnet 'til I die,
I will wear a Killie bonnet, with fuck the Ayr upon it,
wear a Killie bonnet 'til I die.

Tune: 'She'll be Coming Round the Mountain'
There'll be Johnnie Walker whisky in the Cup,
There'll be Johnnie Walker whisky in the Cup,
There'll be Johnnie Walker whisky,
Johnnie Walker whisky,
Johnnie Walker whisky in the Cup – thank fuck.

Tune: 'H.A.P.P.Y.'

*I'm Killie 'til I die, I'm Killie 'til I die, I know I am,
I'm sure I am . . . I'm Killie 'til I die.*

*Killie boys, we are here, woah, woah, Killie boys,
we are here, woah, woah,
Killie boys, we are here, shag your women
and drink your beer . . . Woo-oo-oo-oo-oh!*

*We're here, cos we love Killie. We're here, cos we love
Killie etc.*

*K, I, L – L, I, E . . . and the name of the team is
Kilmarnock FC.*

Tune: 'The Red Flag'

*Oh way up high, up in the sky, we'll keep the blue flag
flying high,
Through rain or muck, we'll fight like fuck, to keep the
blue flag flying high.*

*We'll beat you at home and we'll beat you away, we'll
fuck any bastard that gets in our way,*

We'll drink all your whisky and Newcastle Brown, the
Killie Boys are in town . . . na na na . . . etc

<u>Tune: 'The Happy Wanderer' –</u>
<u>then some Gary Glitter number</u>
I love to go a wandering, along the mountain track, and
as I go I love to sing
. . . the Killie boys are back!
Killie are back, Killie are back, Hello, Hello, It's good to
be back, Killie are back Hello, Hello.

<u>Tune: 'Molly Malone'</u>
In Dublin's fair city, where the girls are so pretty, I first
laid my eyes on sweet Molly Malone,
She wheeled her wheel barrow, through the streets broad
and narrow . . .
Singing . . . Killie! Killie! Killie!

<u>Tune: 'Singing the Blues'</u>
I've never felt more like singing the blues,
The Killie would win – the Ayr would lose,
Oh Killie, you got me singing the blues!

Tune: 'Follow the Van'

My old man, said be a Killie fan,
and don't dilly dally on the way,
We'll take Pittodrie and all that's in it,
we'll take the Jungle in half a minute,
With flick knifes 'n' hammers, chisels and spanners,
we taught the Ayr bastards how to fight,
Oh, you won't take Rugby Park and all that's in it,
cos the Killie boys can fight –Like fuck!

Tune: 'Sailing'

We are Killie, super Killie, no one likes us, we don't care.
We hate Ayr, black bastards, and we'll chase them,
everywhere.

Tune: 'No Awa' Tae Bide Awa''

As I was walking down the Copeland Road, I met a
bunch o' strangers,
And they said to me, "Are you going to see,
The famous Glasgow Rangers?"
So I took a trip to Ibrox Park, to see ma Uncle Willie,
And the boys in blue, got fucked 6-2, from the famous
Ayrshire Killie.

Tune: 'Hersham Boys'

Killie boys, Killie boys, laced up boots and corduroys.
Ayr boys, Ayr boys, Sindy dolls and Tonka toys.

Tune: 'In my Liverpool Home'

In your Glasgow slums . . .
You look in the dustbin for something to eat,
You find a dead cat and you think it's a treat . . .
In your Glasgow slums.
Yer ma's on the game and yer dad's in the nick,
You can't get a job cos your so fuckin thick . . .
In your Glasgow slums.
You shit on the carpet and shit in the bath,
You finger your grannie and think it's a laugh . . .
In your Glasgow slums.
You look in Sue Ryder for something to wear,
Your wife is a junkie, your kids are in care . . .
In your Glasgow slums.

Tune: 'She'll be Coming Round the Mountain'

Singing I come fae Killie no fae Ayr
Singing I come fae Killie no fae Ayr
Singing I come fae Killie, I'm no so fuckin silly,
I come fae Killie no fae Ayr – Thank fuck

<u>Tune: 'Land of Hope and Glory'</u>
We hate Glasgow Rangers, We hate Celtic too,
We hate Ayr United, but Killie we love you!

<u>Tune: 'Marching Through Georgia'</u>
Hello, hello, we are the Killie boys
Hello, hello, we are the Killie boys
And if you are an Ayr fan, surrender or you'll die
We will follow Kilmarnock

<u>Tune: 'Marching Through Georgia'</u>
Hello, hello, we are the Killie boys
Hello, hello, you'll know us by our noise
We're up to our knees in Ayr blood, surrender or you'll die
We are the Ayrshire Killie boys

<u>Tune: 'Island in the Sun'</u>
Oh United came to Killie today,
They're going to show us how to play.
But the Killie boys had the vital spark,
and played the black and whites right off the park.
Oh Glory Glory, in the sun. Killie two, United none.
All the pubs will sing tonight, 'cause Killie knocked shite
out the black and white.

*The Ayr fans came into the town, singin' we're going up
and you're going down.
But Jimmy and Steve said 'Want a bet?', and stuck two
goals in the bastards' net.
Oh Glory Glory, in the sun. Killie two, United none.
All the pubs will sing tonight, 'cause Killie knocked shite
out the black and white.*

*We are the famous Kilmarnock FC, we've won the cup
and the league you see.
But the 2nd team in A*rshire's never had that thrill,
They've won fuck all and never will!
Oh Glory Glory, in the rain. Killie two, united nane.
All the pubs will sing tonight, 'cause Killie knocked shite
out the black and white.*

In praise of players old and new.

<u>Tune: 'D.I.S.C.O.'</u>
*D.A.R.G.O. – He is D.A.R.G.O.
He is D – Delightful, He is A – Amazing, He is R –
Really Brilliant, He is G – Gettin' better
. . . He scores GO-O-OALS*

Tune: 'Hey Jude'

Jesus (hey soos), don't feel so sad,
You took a good team, and made it better.
Remember, we let you into our hearts,
and that's when it started, just getting better
. . . Na na na na na na na, na na na na . . . Jesus (hey soos)
etc.

Tune: 'Auntie Mary Hud a Canary'

Wullie Watters, Wullie Watters, na na na na na na,
Wullie Watters, Wullie Watters, na na na na na na.

Tune: 'The Quartermasters Store'

He's blue, he's white, he used to play for shite,
Ian Durrant, Ian Durrant.

Tune: 'The Quartermasters Store'

When Monty, went up, to lift the Scottish Cup.
We were there, we were there.

Tune: 'Vindaloo'

Dindeleux, Dindeleux – Dindeleux, Dindeleux, na na,
Dindeleux, Dindeleux – Dindeleux, Dindeleux, na na

Dindeleux, Dindeleux – Dindeleux, Dindeleux, na na
We're . . . gonna . . . score . . . one . . . more . . . than . . .
you . . . KILLIE!

Tune: 'Cielito Lindo'
Aye, aye aye aye aye, Cocard is better than Larsson,
And Christophe is better than Tore Andre Flo, and
Christophe is better than anyone!

Tune: 'Robin Hood'
Tommy Burns, Tommy Burns, riding through the glen,
Tommy Burns, Tommy Burns, with another ten,
He's got the flair, You can fuck your Ayr, Tommy Burns,
Tommy Burns, Tommy Burns

Tune: 'Holiday'
Paul, Paul, Paul Di Giacomo – He gets the ball,
He scores the goals – Paul Di Giacomo.

LIVINGSTON

FOUNDED: 1974
(AS MEADOWBANK THISTLE)
NICKNAME: THE LIVVY LIONS
BIGGEST WIN: 6-0 (RAITH ROVERS 1985)
BIGGEST LOSS: 0-8 (HAMILTON ACCIES 1974)
GROUND: ALMONDVALE STADIUM

* * *

Tune: 'Penny Lane'

Almondvale
is in my ears
and in my eyes

up the table
we will surely rise
we love our Almondvale

Chanted by a group of fans at a game in March 2002.
Not sure if it is ironical.

> *Big potential, big potential FC*
> *We've by far the biggest potential*
> *The world has ever seen*

MONTROSE

FOUNDED: 1879
NICKNAME: THE GABLE ENDIES
BIGGEST WIN: 12-0 (VALE OF LEITHEN 1975)
BIGGEST LOSS: 0-13 (ABERDEEN 1951)
GROUND: LINKS PARK

* * *

They call it being realistic in Montrose, or ontrose, as the sign at the entrance to Links Park proclaims.

We're shit, but you're worse than us

And they also have a toast, proclaimed before every game, which is:

Death to the smokie bastards from hell!

They are really not all that keen on Arbroath. And they also sing, on a positive note:

Where ere we go, we fear no foe,
We are the Links Park Dynamo.

MORTON

Founded: 1874
Nickname: The Ton
Biggest win: 11-0 (Carfin Shamrock 1886)
Biggest loss: 1-10 (Port Glasgow 1894,
St Bernard's 1933)
Ground: Cappielow Park
Fanzine: Are We Still Here?

* * *

Tommy Docherty (no, the other one, the Morton-supporting TA foot soldier) writes:

A couple of Morton fans came up with:

Scott Bannerman, do-do-da-do-do
Scott Bannerman, do-do-da-do

against Berwick Rangers (on the 2nd September, 2001) to the tune of 'The Muppets'. Everybody joined in and would sing it for 5 or 6 minutes a couple of times each game. Every time it was chanted, though, a few less people joined in. After 3 games the Cowshed, the players and officials were extremely peed off with it. At the 4th game, against Forfar, the two original guys were on their own and managed to contain themselves for all of 25 minutes, but it was their song and they were gonnae sing it anyway.

After about 3 or 4 minutes of their singing, Morton strung together a neat move and Bannerman smashed a cracker into the Forfar net. The two guys were immensely chuffed and after the celebrations elapsed they went to start it again. This time they were shouted down by all and sundry and the song was never heard again.

It is my opinion that Scott Bannerman was so embarrassed by the song that he only went that far up the park so that he wouldn't have to listen to it.

Tommy also reports on another energy-efficient player for Morton. Just after they had signed Andy Ritchie from Celtic and he seemed a total bargain, they sang to the Celtic fans:

Thank you very much for Andy Ritchie
Thank you very much
Thank you very very very much
Thank you very very much

Tommy doesn't report what they were chanting by

the end of that season, but recently they've been singing:

We hate Coca Cola,
We hate Fanta too . . . and Sprite!
Cause we drink Eldorado,
Mixed with Irn Bru.

Micky Ross sent the following two in from a guy who wishes to remain anonymous and whom he calls "My Morton buddie". He also asks: "Is that an oxymoron?".

I explained that it is not an oxymoron, but a new figure of speech called a doublemoron.

We don't drink whisky and we don't drink gin
We don't drink vodka with the lemonade in
We won't say no to a Bristol Cream
We are the Morton wine team.

Hello hello
How do you do
We are the boys in white and blue
Wherever we go we fear no foe
We are the cowshed aggro (Should that not be agg-a-ro?)

And from the same source, fresh from the cowshed:

We don't carry razors
And we don't carry chains
We just carry brollies
In case it fucking rains

We're not blue
We're not green
We support the local team

And yet more:

"Also, round about the time Mo Johnston almost re-signed for Celtic and then jumped ship and joined the other forces of darkness, we had Rowan Alexander scoring a bundle of goals at Cappielow, accompanied by this little beauty."

We've got Ro
Fuck yer Mo
We've got Ro
Fuck yer Mo
We've got Ro
Fuck yer Mo
Fuck yer Maurice Johnston

Ro Ro Super Ro
Ro Ro Super Ro
Ro Ro Super Ro
Super Alexander

Also, from one of the 'official' club songs as recorded by Hector Nicol in nineteen canteen comes this quality verse –

Goodbye to that old relegation
Goodbye to the days of the flop
Now we're gonna take Greenock Morton
And put them right back at the top

MOTHERWELL

FOUNDED: 1886
NICKNAME: THE WELL
BIGGEST WIN: 12-1 (DUNDEE UNITED 1954)
BIGGEST LOSS: 0-8 (ABERDEEN 1979)
GROUND: FIR PARK
FANZINES: WAITING FOR THE GREAT LEAP
FORWARD, NAY NEED TAE LOSE THE HEID,
ONE STEP BEYOND

* * *

When the idea of Rangers having Catholic players was still fairly radical, they were playing at Fir Park with ten foreigners and Barry Ferguson. When the manager subbed him and another foreign player came on, the chant from the stand, to the tune of 'Chirpy Chirpy Cheep Cheep', was:

Where's yer Proddy gone?
Where's yer Proddy gone?

Answered by the opposite stand with:

> *Not far enough!*
> *Not far enough!*

At a game at Fir Park that I was at some time in the early seventies, the play was so stultifyingly boring that about ten minutes into the second half someone started chanting:

> *Ay, Ay, Ay.* Tiswas *is better than* Swapshop.

Within a few seconds everyone in the ground was at it and the ref had to stop the game for a minute till he and the players had finished laughing. He was laughing so much that he couldn't even blow his whistle.

And it is true as well. *Tiswas* was better than *Swapshop*.

The tune is 'Cielito Lindo' by Quirino Mendoza y Cortés, who lived from 1859 till 1957 and saw a bit or two in his time. I am indebted to Paul Johnson of the *Sunday Post* for this supremely trivial information. You can get the full Spanish version from him.

Not a lot of sympathy here, eh?

> *It's black, it's blue, it's fucking halved in two . . .*
> *Larsson's leg! Larsson's leg!*

*

> *Joe Wark knew my father*
> *My father knew Joe Wark*
> *Joe Wark knew my father*
> *My father knew Joe Wark*
> *Da ra ra ra*

At a 'Well v Sheep match about 10 years ago, someone in the East stand started chanting at Theo Snelders:

> *Yer maw's a whore and yer cat's got rabies.*

Celtic v Motherwell the week after Raith had beaten Celtic on penalties in the League Cup Final . . .

> *He's green, he's white, his penalties are shite –*
> *Paul McStay!*

Or how about:

> *He's fat, he's round, he's worth a million pounds –*
> *(insert name of overweight player)*

Or:
> *He's fat, he's round, he scores at every ground*

And possibly the progenitor of a song that is now sung at every ground to any player (or manager or director) who does not fit the strict physical template laid down by the fans:

<u>Tune: 'Knees Up Mother Brown'</u>

> *Who et all the pies?*
> *Who et all the pies?*
> *You fat bastard*
> *You fat bastard*
> *You et all the pies*

Do not sing the above when Derek Johnstone is in the ground. There is such a thing as sensitivity.

<u>Tune: 'Yellow Submarine'</u>

*All we want is
A ref that isny blind
A ref that isny blind
A ref that isny blind
All we want is etc*

Also sung as, depending if it is the Hunnite or the Timmite tendency you are playing:

All we want is a ref that isny blue

And:

All we want is a ref that isny green

And for a memorable Scottish Cup win which I am proud to say that I attended:

<u>Tune: 'We're No Awa Tae Bide Awa'</u>

*As I was passing Ibrox Park
I heard a mighty clamour
For the boys in blue
Got fucked FIVE-TWO!
By the boys in claret and amber*

Three classics.

'Well, 'Well super 'Well
'Well, 'Well super 'Well
'Well, 'Well super 'Well
Super Motherwell

Tune: 'Lord of the Dance'

We are the boys of the MFC
We hate the Hearts and we canny stand Dundee
We'll beat you all whoever you may be
We are the boys of the MFC

*

We are the 'Well; can't you hear us?
We are the 'Well; can't you hear us?
Walking along, singing a song
Shiting on the Hibees all the way

This is known as 'The Craigneuk Anthem':

Oh the 'Well fans don't carry razors
Oh the 'Well fans don't carry chains
Oh the 'Well fans we just carry shotguns

To blast out the Jam Tart brains
We love you 'Well, we do
We love you 'Well, we do
We love you 'Well, we do
Oh, Motherwell we love you

Been a while since we sang this one, heh heh.

Eeh I oh
Doon ye go
Airdrie, Airdrie

A song for Greenock Morton:

Soap dodgin' bastards
You're only soap dodgin' bastards
Soap dodgin' bastards
You're only soap dodgin' bastards

A song for any player who is suspected of not being 100% heterosexual. There was a Rangers player who heard it a lot.

Wee boys
You only shag wee boys
You only shag wee boys
You only shag wee boys

Have we no shame?

> *Celtic Bhoys Club, Celtic Bhoys Club*
> *They shagged all the boys*
> *Celtic Bhoys Club, Celtic Bhoys Club*
> *They shagged all the boys*

No. And neither did the guilty men at Parkhead, or they would all have snuffed themselves by now.

> *We hate Glasgow Rangers*
> *We hate Celtic too – they're shite!*
> *We hate Airdrieonians*
> *But Motherwell we love you*

*

> *We're the pride of Lanarkshire,*
> *We're the pride of Lanarkshire,*
> *We're the pride of,*
> *We're the pride of,*
> *We're the pride of Lanarkshire,*
> *We're the pride of Lanarkshire*

*

> *Away the lads you should've seen us coming,*
> *We're only here to drink your beer and shag*

your fucking women,
All the lads and lassies had smiles upon their faces,
Walking down the Fir Park Road,
To see the Motherwell aces.

*

You are my 'Well,
My only 'Well,
You make me happy when skies are grey,
You'll know never just how much I love you,
So please don't take my Motherwell away.

Elliot Elliot Eli Elliot,
He gets the ball and scores a goal,
Eli Elliot.

We've got Davie Davie Davie Davie Cooper on the
wing on the wing,
We've got Davie Davie Davie Davie Cooper on the
wing on the wing,
Davie oh Davie Cooper oh Davie Cooper on the wing,
Davie oh Davie Cooper oh Davie Cooper on the wing.

PARTICK THISTLE

FOUNDED: 1876
NICKNAME: THE JAGS, THE MARYHILL MAGYARS
BIGGEST WIN: 16-0 (ROYAL ALBERT, 1931)
BIGGEST LOSS: 0-10 (QUEEN'S PARK, 1881)
GROUND: FIRHILL PARK
FANZINES: SICK IN THE BASIN, WHAT A SENSATION

* * *

According to Chick Young they are 'the cuddly toy of Scottish football', and I agree with him, as they always seem to be left on the conveyor belt when all the rest has gone.

All the away supporters seem to sing about Mary when they go to Firhill, along with other wish-fulfilment fantasies like:

> *We're gonny win the league*
> *We're gonny win the league*
> *You're never gonny beli-e-e-ve it*
> *We're gonny win the league*

Partick, though, did win the league.

MARY FAE MARYHILL

Tune: 'I Love a Lassie'

I know a lassie, a bonnie, bonnie lassie,
She's as tight as a pebble on the wall,
She's got legs like a spider and I would love to ride her,
She's Mary fae Maryhill.

And they don't mess with this bigotry nonsense in Maryhill. They just hate everybody.

FOR THE OLD FIRM

We hate Roman Catholics,
We hate Protestants too (They're Huns!)
We hate Jews and Muslims
Thistle we love you.

And another:

Hello Hello, how do you do
We hate the boys in royal blue
We hate the boys in emerald green
So fuck the Pope and fuck the Queen

The away fans always seem to sing this one as they sit in the Johnny Hubbard stand:

<u>Tune: 'My Old Man's a Dustman'</u>

Johnny Hubbard's magic
He's got a magic hat
He got the Thistle relegated
Then he got the sack

WE WILL FOLLOW

We will follow Thistle
Over Land and Sea
We will follow Thistle
On to victory
All together now . . .

*

We're coming, we're coming
We're coming down the road
When you hear the noise of the Partick Thistle boys
We're coming down the road

*

For ever and ever
We'll follow the Jags
The Partick Thistle
The Harry Wraggs
And all of the promise
That we should fufil
Is to take the Scottish cup
Back home to Maryhill

*

One team in Glasgow
There's only one team in Glasgow
One team in Glasgow

*

We've followed the Thistle for many a day
And watched all the matches home and away
And when the games over and Thistle have won
We'll all go to the tavern and join in the fun
And it's Partick Thistle
Partick Thistle FC
Are by far the greatest team
The world has ever seen

*

Johnnie Lambie's red 'n' yellow army
Johnnie Lambie's red 'n' yellow army
Ooh ooh, Firhill army, ooh ooh, Firhill army

<u>Tune: 'Carnival de Paris'</u>

Na Na Na, Na Na Na, Na Na Na Na Na Na Na Na
Na, Na Na Na Na Na Na Na, Na Na Na Na Na Na
Na, THISTLE!!!

If you want to go to heaven when you die
You must wear a Thistle scarf and tie
You must wear a Thistle bonnet with a thistle on it
(or the more recent – with Fuck the Old Firm on it)
If you want to go to heaven when you die

You know there's a well-known Glasgow football team
Who don't play in blue and don't play in green
Red and Yellow are the colours to be seen
Partick Thistle are that team
(or is it?)
Red and yellow are the colours we love
The colours of Partick Thistle Football Club

*

There's only one Scott McLean
He scores the goals he don't complain

Walking along singing a song
Walking in our Trigger wonderland

For Peter Lindau:

One Swede in Glasgow
There's only one Swede in Glasgow . . .

To St Mirren:

Did you bring us any drugs?

To Clyde:

Are you watching Gypsy scum?
Are you watching Gypsy scum?
Can we play you every week?
Can we play you every week?

To Kilmarnock:

You only sing when you're farming
Sing when you're farming
You only sing when you're farming

To Arbroath:

You only sing when you're fishing
Sing when you're fishing
You only sing when you're fishing

To Livingston:

Meadowbank, wank wank wank
Meadowbank, wank wank wank

PETERHEAD

FOUNDED: 1891
NICKNAME: THE BLUE TOON
BIGGEST WIN: 17-1 (FORT WILLIAM 1998)
BIGGEST LOSS: NOT RECORDED
(SO IT MUST HAVE BEEN A CRACKER)
GROUND: BALMOOR STADIUM

*   *   *

More realism, but not a lot of the romance and hope that keeps most of us going.

THE MIDDLE OF THE LEAGUE SONG

We're not going down and we're not going up
We won't win the league and we won't win the cup

Micky Ross sent me the following.

"Still commuting, still reading *Two Andy Gorams*. And I don't want to sound like a proof reader, but Peterhead play at Balmoor Stadium (not Balmore)."

Everyone's a bloody critic. It says Balmoor now. Cheers, Micky. He continues:

"The only song in their section is one I used to sing in my days down South as a Wimbledon fan, which had another couple of lines . . .

We're not going down and we're not going up
We won't win the league and we won't win the cup
We're not very good in fact we're bad
We are the Wombles, we're mad
Na na na na naaa naaaa,
Na na na na naaa naaaa . . .

etc., ad infinitum, in a stupid, barmy, 'just out of a secured establishment' kind of voice."

See precise? See Micky? He goes on:

"Not sure of the tune either, but I could always sing it for you someday and see if you recognise it! Don't know if the Blue Tooners sing the last three lines and I'd be almost certain that the fourth line may have to be modified. Would have thought that 'Drummond's Pyscho Crew' would show empathy with line five though. Line 6 isn't part of the song. Unless you can make it scan."

QUEEN OF THE SOUTH

FOUNDED: 1919
NICKNAME: THE DOONHAMERS
BIGGEST WIN: 11-1 (STRANRAER 1932)
BIGGEST LOSS: 2-10 (DUNDEE 1962)
GROUND: PALMERSTON PARK.

* * *

There are a couple of quasi-official songs, one from a group called The Only Team in the Bible (Luke, chapter 11, verse 13 and Matthew chapter 12, verse 42, if you are interested), but having listened to them on the web I've decided not to inflict them on you. This is one which the fans actually sing:

Tune: 'The Man Who Broke the Bank at Monte Carlo'

We support the local football team and we shout
'C'mon the Queens!'
They never win it seems, they shatter all our dreams;
Here, there and everywhere,

You can hear the boys and girls declare,
'God Save the Queens from relegation!'

And one from a desperate period in the club's history, though the sense of humour was still there:

WE'RE GAN DOON

We're gan doon
We're gan doon
An' you're no!

Some anonymous Doonhamer (ie, I've forgotten who it was) sent me the following, as he was miffed at the paucity of Queen of the South's songs. Can't say I'm much impressed. I even had to put in the capital letters.

clap clap clap clap clap clap clap clap clap Queens
clap clap clap clap clap clap clap clap clap Queens
clap clap clap clap clap clap clap clap clap Queens
clap clap clap clap clap clap clap clap clap Queens
clap clap clap clap clap clap clap clap clap Queens
clap clap clap clap clap clap clap clap clap Queens
clap clap clap clap clap clap clap clap clap Queens
clap clap clap clap clap clap clap clap clap Queens
clap clap clap clap clap clap clap clap clap Queens
clap clap clap clap clap clap clap clap clap Queens

"Repeat until in pain", he then suggests. And then goes on:

clap clap clap clap clap clap clap clap clap clap clap clap
clap clap clap clap clap clap clap clap clap clap clap clap
clap clap clap clap clap clap clap clap clap clap clap clap
clap clap clap clap clap clap clap clap clap clap clap clap
clap clap clap clap clap clap clap clap clap clap clap clap
clap clap clap clap [sambastyle]

or

We are the Queen of the South clap clap clap clap

One from Leith Doonhamer:
During the foot and mouth crisis we were playing Fartick at Firhill. The cheeky Maryhill wags started a chant of "sheep shagging bastards" to which we replied . . .

"No sheep in Dumfries
oh there are no sheep in Dumfries . . ."

Bunch of spendthrifts here, it would appear. I've no idea of the tune.

We are known for our manners,
We like to spend our tanners,

We are respected wherever we may go, so –

We may travel by the railway line,
Doors and windows open wide – open wide!
Hear the men and women shout –
"See the Dumfries boys are out!"
We are the Dumfries boys.

QUEEN'S PARK

FOUNDED: 1867
NICKNAME: THE SPIDERS
BIGGEST WIN: 16-0 (ST PETER'S 1885)
BIGGEST LOSS: 0-9 (MOTHERWELL [YES!] 1930)
GROUND: HAMPDEN PARK
FANZINE: THE WEB

* * *

Fraser Gibson is a trombonist and plays while the Spiders fans are singing:

Enjoy yourself, it's later than you think!
Enjoy yourself, while you're still in the pink!

They also sing:

Allez les Hoops!
Allez les Hoops!

This Francophonic chant was the Spiders' contribution to Glasgow's Year of Culture. When they played in their red away strips they sang:

Allez les Rouges
Allez les Rouges
Allez les Rouges
Allez
Allez les Rouges
Allez les Rouges
Allez les Rouges
Allez

Now they play in their Irn Bru tops, a fetching confection in electric blue and sodium orange. They now chant:

Come on the Bru boys! (clap clap clap clap)
Come on the Bru boys! (clap clap clap clap)

Und so weiter into infinity . . .

RAITH ROVERS

FOUNDED: 1883
NICKNAME: THE ROVERS
BIGGEST WIN: 10-1 (COLDSTREAM 1954)
BIGGEST LOSS: 2-11 (MORTON 1936)
GROUND: STARK'S PARK
FANZINE: STARK'S BARK

* * *

I am indebted for the following paragraph to a fanzine titled *Elvis Was a Rovers' Fan*. Unfortunately, none of the songs have survived.

It can surely be no coincidence that on the only day Elvis set foot in Britain, at Prestwick Airport, the Rovers were playing away to Ayr United. Unfortunately, Elvis forgot about the time-zone problem and missed kick-off by three hours. Some have linked the beginning of his decline to that moment. Amongst his many tribute songs to the Rovers were: 'I Don't Have A Wooden Stand', 'What Made Kirkcaldy Famous (made a loser out of me)', 'Blue Christmas' and 'Crying In The Chapel Tavern'.

When things are going well for Raith, which isn't often, they sing Geordie Munro. Here are some notes on it, as well as other musings, from John Greer, a Stark's Park legend, sent to me by Micky Ross. In the interest of not getting sued, I've left out the stories about John that I was also sent. Here he goes.

My name is Munro; my home is in Fife,
I wanted to make a new start in my life,
I wanted to go to the U S of A,
when a certain wee lassie did say –

Chorus
Oh no no no Geordie Munro,
no-no no-no no-no my wee laddie,
I don't want to go to Idaho,
I rather stay here in KIRKCALDY.

Now I determined, I'd not stay in Fife,
I wanted that lassie to be my sweet wife,
So one day we went for a walk down the Glen,
And I asked her all over again.

Chorus

And 'though we'd been happy, if I had my way,
We'd still emigrate to the U S of A,
But if ever I'd thought of old Idaho,
The voices in chorus sing No !

Chorus

John goes on: "This is the traditional song sung by the Raith Rovers supporters. This is the song that rang out at Ibrox, on Sunday 27th November 1994, when the Rovers won the Coca-Cola Cup by beating Celtic. The following year it was in the Faroes, Iceland and Munich, as our great European adventure took in more ties than anyone could imagine. In fact we set a record for a Scottish team reaching Europe, by qualifying for a third round in our debut season.

The song is an old Scottish favourite that was part of The Alexander Brothers stage set. It is quite interesting that Geordie Munro is treated as some kind of hero by the Rovers fans, with the like of fanzine columns written under his name and supporters groups, who sponsor matches, e.g. The Neeburs of Geordie Munro.

When Geordie is, plainly, the villain who wants to emigrate away from Kirkcaldy and, his girlfriend wants to "stay here in Kirkcaldy".

In 1992 Raith Rovers produced a tape of favourite "ROVERS' SONGS". On it and available for the first in over 30 years was a Raith Rovers song similar to the original Hearts song.

Around this time Rovers would enter the pitch to this tune:

In the toon of Kirkcaldy there is a fitba' team,
The finest team in Scotland,
Raith Rovers is their name,
They play doon at Stark's Park,
And if you go there on a Saturday,
This is what you'll hear

Chorus
Raith Rovers – Raith Rovers,
Let's give the boys a hand,
Raith Rovers – Raith Rovers,
The best team in the land.

Also on the tape are the usual favourites of most teams.

Plus one which tells, *"men will live for evermore because of Kirkcaldy."*

Another favourite has always been

> *Wise men say,*
> *Only fools rush in,*
> *But I can't help falling in love with you.*
> *ROVERS – ROVERS etc 'til fade*

In recent times, while the Rovers have been in the 2nd Division, the younger element of the Rovers' fans have taken to singing this little ditty.

> *My garden shed, is bigger than this!*
> *O' my garden shed is bigger than this!*
> *It's got a door,*
> *And a window!*
> *My garden shed is bigger than this!*
>
> *My garden shed, is bigger than this!*
> *O' my garden shed is bigger than this!*
>
> *It's got a seat,*
> *and yours hasny!*
> *My garden shed is bigger than this!*

This is sung at away grounds, to have a go at opponent's grounds and small "box"-like stands.

This song even prompted a request from a BBC Scotland researcher on the Rovers' Official Website for someone from the fan base that had a Garden Shed that they used as a "Temple to the Rovers".

Jim Rowbotham also sent in the garden shed song, with the following comment:
> "Crap I know, but my laddie
> forced me to send it in.
> Cheers
> JIM."

Ach, bugger it, here are some stories about John Greer anyway. I'm not saying who sent them, though the initials JC might have some relevance.

"The best is the true story that he asked the doctors NOT to induce Alison so that he could travel from his home in Yorkshire to see the Rovers take on St Mirren in a Scottish Cup quarter-final in 1987.

The doctors agreed to his request, and thankfully Alison gave birth to Amy a few days later.

Other stories.

John has in the past got himself onto radio phone-ins by telling the producer that he was either a Celtic/ Rangers/Hibs/Hearts fan and then hit the panel with his real topic, which is usually the Rovers.

One day however, he got through ostensibly to talk about Kenny Miller (then a Hibbee threatening to move to Rangers) and instead had a real go at Gordon Smith for his continued praise in commentary of the players he is the agent for.

At the end of the heated discussion involving John and Mr Smith, Richard Gordon was heard on air "Don't know how that one got through!!"

He's one of about only 100 fans who can claim to have been at all 6 of Rovers' UEFA Cup matches.

He has his name on a seat in the South Stand at Stark's Park, and his name (and those of his two daughters) on commemorative bricks under the South Stand.

He's the world's best namedropper.

As steward at Gullane Golf Club, he has met (and had his photo taken with) some incredibly famous celebrities including Ian Botham, Alan Shearer and Michael Jordan.

The best however was him phoning up and saying that he had just met Jesus – Jesus Sanjuan of Kilmarnock FC who was down at the club with his pal Sergio Garcia. He once met up with Ivo Den Bieman, then of Rovers' biggest rivals, Dunfermline Athletic.

John's youngest daughter Amy was with him (she'd be around 6 or 7 years old at the time).

Big Ivo tried to explain to Amy that he was a professional footballer, and from the back of his car produced a match programme on which he was the cover star.

Cue much embarrassment when Amy piped up 'Look Dad, he plays for Scumfermline'."

To the opposition fans the Raith fans sing:

We know who you are
and we know where you've been
You're the worst dressed supporters
that we've ever seen

Get a life, get a life, get a life!

More from Jim Clark:

Could you go a Coca-Cola Paul McStay?
Could you go a Coca-Cola Paul McStay?
Could you go a Coca-Coca?
Go a Coca-Cola?
Could you go a Coca-Cola Paul McStay?

Papin missed a penalty
Papin missed a penalty
Papin missed a penalty
Papin missed a penalty

(repeat ad nauseum)

Jim says: "NB - this commemorates that in the match at the Olympic Stadium in Munchen, and prior to Daniel Lennon putting the Rovers 1-0 up, JP Papin did indeed miss a penalty (conceded Amoruso style by Ronnie Coyle, for which he collected a booking that ruled him out of the next Euro tie!)

And finally . . . to the tune of 'Always Look on the Bright Side of Life' and aimed at Scumfermline fans:

You were born on the wrong side of Fife

RANGERS

FOUNDED: 1873
NICKNAMES: THE GERS, THE TEDDY BEARS
BIGGEST WIN: 14-2 (BLAIRGOWRIE 1934)
BIGGEST LOSS: 2-10 (AIRDRIE 1886)
GROUND: IBROX STADIUM
FANZINE: FOLLOW, FOLLOW AND LOTS OF OTHERS

* * *

Celtic's winning their way to Seville produced the odd nasty comment, like:

> *Tell all the Tims you know*
> *Euros and Giros don't go.*

And the jocular threat, a little less meaningful, as a lot of the wives were there.

> *Tell all the Tims you know*
> *We'll be shagging your wives when you go.*

Then there was the nationalistic approach to the event:

Scotland – this is your country – the home of great poets, writers, engineers and inventors of almost everything we take for granted to make our lives comfortable and convenient.

A land of clean fresh air, beautiful mountainous scenery, crystal clear water which provides the base for Scotch whisky, the most popular drink in the world, shared by friends wherever they meet to toast and celebrate memorable occasions.

So today lift your eyes and see this place where you live, see how good it really is at this moment, raise a glass of whisky, reflect on what we have, how good it could be, appreciate all it's beauty and glory.

Realise just how different it looks and feels today. How it seems just that little bit better.

Is the air fresher and purer?

Does the sun seem brighter?

Yes it is —

Why?

Because there is 50,000 fewer tattie-howking, immigrant, manky TIMS in the place.

THAT'S WHY!!!

And, of course, they had their small t troubles, as well:

<u>Tune: 'If You're Happy and You Know It, Clap Your Hands'</u>

If the team can't beat Kilmarnock, blame the ref
If John Hartson is a diver, blame the ref
If O'Neill jumps up and down,
Like a mad demented clown,
It's because they're out to get us, blame the ref
If we cannae beat the Rangers, blame the ref
If Rab Douglas is a crapbag, blame the ref
If Bobo can't mark Moore,
And Larsson is so poor
It's because the world's against us, blame the ref
If our fans riot at Ajax, blame the police
If they do the same in Vigo, blame the police
If they do the same again,
When they come home on the plane,
Well, we all know cops are masons, blame the police
If Neil Lennon is a nutjob, blame the press,
If Valhaagren is a robber, blame the press
If Bobby Petta and Mjalby
Get nicked for 'gieing it laldy'
It's all a Proddy plot, blame the press

And another sharp nip:

<u>Tune: 'Jingle Bells'</u>

Flying through the air
On a Euro chartered flight
Smoking in the bogs
The fans begin to fight

Bells and sirens ring
The pilot calls Mayday
This is what you can expect
When you see the Celtic play

Oh, Jingle Bells, Jingle Bells, Jingle all the way
Oh what fun it is to see their fans get put away
Oh Jingle Bells, Jingle Bells, Jingle all the way
And now the players get involved
and a camera's gone astray

And also:

You are the Celtic
The Glasgow Celtic
You like to smoke fags, on aeroplanes
Newcastle nightclubs
A team of jailbirds
Please don't take my camera away . . .

<u>Tune: 'Happiness'</u>
(a tribute to Inverness Caledonian beating Celtic)

Oh happiness, happiness
The greatest gift that I possess
I thank the team from Inverness
For bringing me so much happiness

*

Whenever I'm in times of trouble,
Mother Mary comes to me,
Singing Glasgow Celtic 1, Caley 3.
Celtic 1, Caley 3,
Celtic 1, Caley 3,
Glasgow Celtic 1, Caley 3.

THE NICE BILLY BOYS

<u>(To be sung very quietly to the tune</u>
<u>'Marching Through Georgia'.)</u>

Hello, hello, we are the Billy Boys
Hello, hello, we don't like making noise
We're not up to our knees in any kind of
strangers' blood at all
We are peaceful and friendly

This is not too peaceful or friendly, but the joy of these kind of insults is that they are interchangeable with the Huns. There are hundreds of them.

I'd rather be Bin Laden than a Tim

During the Souness era at Ibrox there was a chant which went:

Sou—ness! Sou—ness!

It was kind of primeval leadership acknowledgement a bit akin, to my ears, to:

Seig heil!
Seig heil!

But this was defused for me one day when a somewhat overweight photographer was making his plodding way to the goal to ply his trade. He was, in fact, so overweight that his colleagues called him The Bouncy Castle. The Ibrox crowd are sharp tongued and cruel, as well as being no respecters of persons. Observing his girth and his waddle, the entire crowd chanted:

Su—mo! Su—mo!

On another occasion there was a team of sub-pubescent, baton-twirling girls who were on for far too long. Becoming impatient and trying to hurry their exit, the audience started singing:

> *Get it up ye*
> *Get it up ye*
> *Get it up ye*
> *Get it up ye while yer young!*

And achieved their aim in no short order.

An outdated one now, but a grudging word of praise for a Celtic team, the only one I have ever heard from any Rangers supporter. I cannot recall a vice-versa from Celtic.

Tune: 'John Brown's Body'

> *Celtic's only decent team were called the Lisbon Lions*
> *Now their ground's a pig-sty built with corrugated iron*
> *It smells of shite and urine and it rattles in the wind*
> *And it'll all come tumbling down*
> *Glory glory for the cheapskates*
> *Glory glory for the cheapskates*
> *Glory glory for the cheapskates*
> *Their stadium's falling down*

There's only one Jorge Cadete
He's got hair like spaghetti
He's Portuguese and he's one of these
Walking in a Laudrup wonderland

*

If ye cannae dae the bouncy you're a Tim!
If ye cannae dae the bouncy you're a Tim!
If ye cannae dae the bouncy, cannae dae the bouncy,
Cannae dae the bouncy you're a Tim!
Ooh!!!
BOUNCY, BOUNCY, BOUNCY, BOUNCY,
Na Na Na La Na Na!
BOUNCY, BOUNCY, BOUNCY, BOUNCY,
Na Na Na La Na Na!

None of the following allegations have the ring of truth about them, do they?

Pierre! There's only one Pierre!
He takes it up the rear!
Cos he's a fuckin' queer!

There's only one Henrik Larsson
He's got a face like a Martian!

WHO'S THAT TEAM
THEY CALL THE RANGERS

Who's that team we all adore
They're the boys in royal blue and they are
Scotland's gallant few
And we are out to show the world what we can do
So bring on the Hibs, the Hearts, the Celtic
Bring on Spaniards by the score
And we will hope that every game,
we will immortalise the name
Of the boys that wear the famous royal blue

THE SASH

For it's here I am an Orangeman
Just come across the sea
For singing and for dancing
I hope that I'll please thee
I can sing and dance with any man
As I did in days of yore
And its on the twelfth I long to wear
The sash my father wore
It is old but it is beautiful
And it's colours they are fine
It was worn at Derry, Aughrim, Enniskillen

And the Boyne
My Father wore it as a youth
In bygone days of yore
And its on the twelfth I long to wear
The sash my father wore
For it's now I'm going to leave you
Good luck to you I'll say
And when I'm on the ocean deep
I hope for me you'll pray
I'm going to my native land
To a place they call Dromore
Where on the twelfth I long to wear
The sash my father wore
Whenever I come back again
My brethren here to see
I hope to find old Orange style
They will always welcome me
My favourite tune's 'Boyne Water'
But to please me more and more,
And make my Orange heart full glad
With the Sash my Father wore

THE SASH (2)

It is old but it is beautiful, it's red, it's white and it's blue
It's worn on the slopes of Ibrox Park
And a place called Parkhead too
My father wore it as a youth in the bygone days of yore
And it's on display every Saturday every time
the Rangers score

*

For ever and ever we'll follow the Gers
The Glasgow Rangers, the Teddy Bears
For we will be mastered by whom
by no Fenian bastards
We'll keep the Blue Flag flying high

*

Soooooo, bring on the Hibs, the Hearts, the Celtic
Bring on the Spaniards by the score
Barcelona, Real Madrid
Who the hell are you trying to kid
For we're out to show the world what we can do

FOLLOW FOLLOW

Follow, follow, we will follow Rangers
Everywhere, anywhere we will follow on
Dundee, Hamilton, even up to Aberdeen
If they go to Dublin we will follow on
For there's not a team like the Glasgow Rangers
No not one, and there never shall be one

Celtic know all about their Troubles
We will fight till the day is done
For there's not a team like the Glasgow Rangers
No not one and there never shall be one

Follow, follow, we will follow Rangers
Everywhere, anywhere we will follow on
Dundee, Hamilton, even up to Aberdeen
If they go to Dublin we will follow on

THE BLUE FLAG

Hello, hello, how do you do
We are the boys in royal blue
Where e'er we go, we fear no foe
We'll keep the blue flag flying high

Oh flying high up in the sky
We'll keep the blue flag flying high
Where e'er we go, we fear no foe
We'll keep the blue flag flying high

This one is for Andy Cameron, the world's nicest Bluenose and a man whom I have heard singing it.

EVERY OTHER SATURDAY

Every other Saturday's my half day off
And it's off to the match I go
Happily we wander down the Copland Road
Me and my wee pal Joe
We love to see the lassies with the blue scarfs on
We love to hear the boys all roar
But I don't have to tell that the best of all
We love to see the Rangers score
Me Oh Me Oh Me Oh My –
Oh how we love to see them try
We love to see the lassies with the blue scarfs on
We love to hear the boys all roar
But I don't have to tell that the best of all
We love to see the Rangers score

We've won the Scottish League almost every time
The League Cup is as simple too
We give some exhibitions in the Scottish Cup
We are the Cup winners true
And when the Rangers win the European Cup
As we've done with the one before
We'll gather round at Ibrox 50,000 strong to give the boys
An Ibrox roar.

Me Oh Me Oh Me Oh My –
Oh how we love to see them try
We love to see the lassies with the blue scarfs on
We love to hear the boys all roar
But I don't have to tell that the best of all
We love to see the Rangers score

THE BLUEBELLS ARE BLUE

All the bluebells are blue,
All the bluebells are blue,
All the bluebells are blue,
All the bluebells are blue,

Repeat until you are what colour in the face?

ROSS COUNTY

FOUNDED: 1929
NICKNAMES: COUNTY, THE STAGGIES
BIGGEST WIN: 11-0 (ST CUTHBERT'S WANDERERS 1993)
BIGGEST LOSS: 1-10 (INVERNESS THISTLE)
GROUND: VICTORIA PARK
FANZINE: OVER THE BRIDGE

* * *

We hate Caley Thistle,
We hate Livi too, (they're shite!)
We hate Ayr United,
But County we love you . . .

And a special just for Caley games:

The wheels on your house go round and round . . .

Also:

I'd rather be a gyppo than a tink,
I'd rather be a gyppo than a tink, etc

<u>Tune: 'The Fields of Athenry'</u>

Low lie the fields of Jubilee
Where once we watched Derek Adams play
With Ferries on the wing
We had dreams and songs to sing
It's all glory round the fields of Jubilee

<u>Tune: 'Singing the Blues'</u>

I've never felt more like sinking the booze,
When County win and Caley lose,
Ooh County, you've got me sinking the booze!

This is one that rugby fans have been singing for decades. I don't know how the Staggies got hold of it, but as far as I know it is unique to them in football

YOGI BEAR

<u>Tune: 'Camptown Races'</u>

I know a bear that you don't know
Yogi, Yogi

I know a bear that you don't know
Yogi, Yogi Bear
Yogi, Yogi Bear
Yogi, Yogi Bear
I know a bear that you don't know
Yogi, Yogi Bear

Yogi's got a girlfriend
Suzi, Suzi
Yogi's got a girlfriend
Suzi, Suzi Bear
Suzi, Suzi Bear
Suzi, Suzi Bear
Yogi's got a girlfriend
Suzi, Suzi Bear

Yogi likes them tall and blonde
Danni, Danni
Yogi likes them tall and blonde
Danni, Danni Behr
Danni, Danni Behr
Danni, Danni Behr
Yogi likes them tall and blonde
Danni, Danni Behr

Suzi likes it in the fridge
Polar, Polar
Suzi likes it in the fridge
Polar, Polar bear
Polar, Polar bear
Polar, Polar bear
Suzi likes it in the fridge
Polar, Polar bear

Suzi likes it in a car
Panda, Panda
Suzi likes it in a car
Panda, Panda Bear
Panda, Panda Bear
Panda, Panda Bear
Suzi likes it in a car
Panda, Panda Bear
Panda, Panda Bear
Panda, Panda Bear
Suzi likes it in a car
Panda, Panda Bear

Suzi supports the Caley tinks
Hard to, hard to
Suzi supports the Caley tinks
Hard to, hard to bear
Hard to, hard to bear

Hard to, hard to bear
Suzi supports the Caley tinks
Hard to, hard to bear

*

Neale Cooper's Baldy Army
Neale Cooper's Baldy Army
Neale Cooper's Baldy Army
Baldy Army, {clap clap clap}
Baldy Army, {clap clap clap}
Baldy Army, {clap clap clap}
Baldy Army, {clap clap clap}
Baldy . . .

And so on, until a new song starts, or your hands get sore.

He scores with his head, and his left, and his right
Geordie Shaw is dynamite

ST JOHNSTONE

FOUNDED: 1884
NICKNAME: THE SAINTS
BIGGEST WIN: 9-0 (ALBION ROVERS 1946)
BIGGEST LOSS: 1-10 (THIRD LANARK 1903)
GROUND: McDIARMID PARK
FANZINE: BLUE HEAVEN

* * *

At McDiarmid Park, Scotland's first all-covered ground, the fans used to sing:

We've got one, we've got two,
We've got three more stands than you.

And a tribute to a hero, known as 'The Legend':

He's white, he's blue
He likes a pint or two
Roddy Grant! Roddy Grant!

A couple of years back, for no reason that anyone will admit to, they sang:

> *Ding dong the witch is dead*
> *Ding dong the witch is dead*
> *Ding dong the wicked witch is dead*

And one from Wee John, delivered to me at a Tartan Army 7-a-side tourney in Perth.

BYE, BYE DUNDEE

> *We had only just begun,*
> *when Pele made it Number One*
> *Bye, bye Dundee*
> *Glory to the boys in blue, as Derek made it Number Two*
> *Bye, bye Dundee*
> *Gemmill couldn't believe what he was seein'*
> *As Derek headed Number Fuckin' Three in*
> *And as the Saints went up for more*
> *Derek made it Number Four*
> *Dundee, bye bye.*

ST MIRREN

FOUNDED: 1877
NICKNAME: THE BUDDIES
BIGGEST WIN: 15-0 (GLASGOW UNIVERSITY 1960)
BIGGEST LOSS: 0-9 (RANGERS 1897)
GROUND: ST MIRREN PARK
FANZINE: SAINTS QUARTERLY

* * *

To be sung at opposition supporters whose grounds do not meet the 10,000 all-seater stadium criteria necessary to enter the SPL. Buddies take blow-up seats to Brockville, for instance.

Tune: 'Camptown Races'

We've got 10,000 seats
You've no, you've no
We've got 10,000 seats
Yoooou've no

They also sing:

> *We're black, we're white*
> *Our team's a load of shite*

And for a negative viewpoint, sometimes just for a change they'll sing:

> *We're white, we're black*
> *Our team's a load of cack*

St Mirren also get a salutation from Partick which I think is unique. The Thistle fans chant:

> *Dirty Paisley junkies!*

And sing:

> *Sing when you're fixing*
> *You only sing when you're fixing*
> *Sing when you're fixing*
> *You only sing when you're fixing*

STENHOUSEMUIR

FOUNDED: 1884
NICKNAME: THE WARRIORS
BIGGEST WIN: 9-2 (DUNDEE UNITED 1937)
BIGGEST LOSS: 2-11 (DUNFERMLINE 1930)
GROUND: OCHILVIEW PARK

* * *

Could not find a single unique song for the Warriors. Shame, eh?

A person calling him or herself Fudge the Warrior read the above and submitted these. I inserted <u>all</u> of the capital letters and <u>all</u> of the punctuation.

We're maroon, we're white, we're fuckin' dynamite.

John McVeigh's barmy army.

Brockville's falling down. It's falling down.

If u hate the Falkirk Bairns clap your hands.

We're by far the greatest team, the world has ever seen.

Gladstone Road is our delight,
Our colours are maroon and white,
We love to sing we love to fight,
For we r the Stenny, boot boys!
We're not orange. We're not green.
We support our local team.

Another Warrior, this one purporting to be The Jollywell Church of Chaffit, sent my mate Kosmik, under the impression that he had compiled the last edition of this book, a whole bunch of stuff, pages and pages of it, including this song:

EVELYN

A Tribute To Evelyn Morrison,
Stenhousemuir's Greatest Goal-Sniffer.
<u>Tune: 'Alison' by Elvis Costello</u>

Oh, it's so funny to be manly after so long, girl
And the way you look I understand you don't wear
football boots
Box to box you made my world go round
And those high heels they really did suit

I'm not gonna be too fundamentalist
'Bout what sociologists swear are just traits
Cos I don't know if it's wrong to wear make-up
I only know you're one of the greats

Evelyn, I know the press is killing you
Evelyn, maroon and blue

And they say you're under floodlights now
They say that's the future but I doubt it very much
That's about as likely as transsexuals on the telly
And an Alva man who doesn't go Dutch
Sometimes I wish I could stop you from scoring
For the way you slobber all your team-mates
I think someone better put out the spotlight
If female impersonator signifies gay

Evelyn, I know the press is killing you
Evelyn, maroon and blue

Before you ask, I haven't got a scooby what it is all about. I'm just trying to be democratic and give everyone a chance. People who are seen as strange need love also, and teams to support. They too have dreams and songs to sing.

STIRLING ALBION

FOUNDED: 1945
NICKNAME: THE BINOS
BIGGEST WIN: 20-0 (SELKIRK 1984)
BIGGEST LOSS: 0-9 (DUNDEE UNITED 1967)
GROUND: FORTHBANK STADIUM
FANZINE: RAVE ON

* * *

Sung to the tune of 'Blue Moon', this is a song directed at the Bairns fans after they lost to Kilmarnock in the Scottish Cup and then the Binos subsequently thrashed Killie in the following season's League Cup.

Six, Two – what was the score with you?
We beat the Killie Six, Two.
We beat the Killie Six, Two.

*

Let's all do the Conga
Stirling's getting stronger

Na, na, na, na,
Na, na, na, na.
No silverware, no silverware
The Bairns have got no silverware
From Brockville Park to George Square
The Bairns have got no silverware

*

Alex Bone, Alex Bone
Alex, Alex Bone
He scores a goal,
Eats a gammon roll
Alex, Alex Bone

Tune: 'Hark The Herald Angels Sing'

Gareth's steaming up the wing
Alex's waiting in the box
(Geraghty's picked up a knock)
Hark the mighty Binos sing
Ross is there as well
Where this ends up who can tell
Bloody hell and bugger me
Ross just scored from off his knee

Hark the mighty Binos sing
The goalie didnae see a thing

Tune: 'Rudolph the Red-Nosed Reindeer'

Cremin the big-eared schoolboy
Had a giant pair of lugs
And if you ever saw them
They looked like handles on a mug
All of the other Binos
Laughed at him and called him names
They never thought young Cremin
Would be picked to play a game

Then one rainy afternoon
The Binos played away
2-1 down and Stewart's plea
'Blair please score a goal for me'
Yes, at the National Stadium
Blair came on and scored a goal
And all the Binos loved him
Let's all hope he's on a roll

Tune: 'White Christmas'

I'm dreaming of a big striker
Just like the ones we used to cheer
When Gus McMillan would rise above them
And Hughes would fill them all with fear
I'm dreaming of a new left back
Why did Paul Deasey have to go
May Ray Stewart lead us to the light
And may all our full backs not be right

THE WILD BINO

Tune: 'The Wild Rover'

Well I've been a red boy for many's a year
And I've spent all my money on football and beer
Well I get up early on a Saturday
I put on my scarf and I watch the boys play

Chorus
And it's Stirling Albion
(clap, clap, clap, clap)
Stirling Albion FC

They're by far the greatest team
The world has ever seen.

Now win lose or draw boys – we'll always be there
Cause for Celtic or Rangers well we dinnae care
We'll have a few pints on a Saturday night
Along with the boys in the red and the white

Chorus

Now you can keep Falkirk, Rangers or Chelsea
And I'll tell you something I hope you'll agree
There's a team up at Forthbank that we go and see
And they call themselves Stirling Albion FC

Chorus

MEET THE GANG

Meet the gang 'cos the boys are here
The boys to entertain you
With Marky and Boomer and Woodsy on the wing
And Alex Bone who's the king, king, king
No Rangers, no Celtic, no Hibs, no Hearts, Dundee

We are the boys – the Stirling Albion FC
'Cos meet the gang cause the boys are here
The boys to entertain you
A – L – B – I – O – N, boys to entertain you

*

I'm no Bairn – I'm a red
Singing I'm no a Bairn – I'm a red
Singing I'm no a Bairn and I'm no fucking caring
I'm no Bairn – I'm a red
Thank fuck

*

Hello, hello – have you heard right
About the boys in red and white

*

Their famous names go on and on
The one and only Albion

*

Hello, hello – have you been told
About the boys in black and gold
Their famous name goes tra la la
The fucking shitey Alloa

STRANRAER

FOUNDED: 1870
NICKNAME: THE BLUE
BIGGEST WIN: 7-0 (BRECHIN 1965)
BIGGEST LOSS: 1-11 (QUEEN OF THE SOUTH 1932)
GROUND: STAIR PARK

* * *

Couldn't find any Stranraer songs either. Maybe they are away with the ferries . . .

SWINDON TOWN

This is the answer to the question 'What league side doesn't have any of the letters of the word "mackerel" in its name?'

FOUNDED: 1881
NICKNAME: THE ROBINS
RECORD VICTORY: 10-1 V FARNHAM UTD BREWERIES
(AWAY), FA CUP 1ST ROUND REPLAY,
28 NOVEMBER 1925
RECORD LEAGUE VICTORY: 9-1 V LUTON TOWN
(HOME), DIVISION 3 (S), 28 AUGUST 1920
RECORD DEFEAT: 1-10 V MANCHESTER CITY (AWAY),
FA CUP 4TH ROUND REPLAY, 25 JANUARY 1930
GROUND: THE COUNTY GROUND.
FANZINE: THE MAGIC ROUNDABOUT

* * *

'Hello', I hear you think, 'Swindon's not in the Scottish leagues at all'. If you have a problem with that, ignore this bit. WillfaeSwindon and I have been e-mailing and any Tartan Army foot soldier that asks a favour gets it, OK?

This was the occasion when 8,000 Swindon fans outsang 41,000 Man U supporters in a League Cup match at Old Trafford. Allow Will his dreams.

<u>Tune: 'Big Ben'</u>

Shit ground, no fans,
Shit ground, no fans.

Will also tells of when Swindon Town were bottom of the league and the opposition started up with the customary:

Going down. Going down. Going down.

The Swindon fans replied with:

So are we. So are we. So are we.

Even the players are a bit strange, according to Will:

One time a specialist had declared on Sky Sports or something that he had studied the team picture of Swindon Town and that one of the team was in fact an alien. Cue endless renditions of:

'Jimmy Glass is an alien'

to which he would put his hands on his head and point his fingers to simulate antennae.

TARTAN ARMY

FOUNDED: SOMETIME IN THE SEVENTIES
NICKNAME: THE TA
BIGGEST WIN AGAINST ENGLAND: 17-0
(MADE THAT ONE UP)
BIGGEST LOSS AGAINST *ENGLAND*: 3-9 (DIDN'T MAKE
THAT ONE UP. WAS THERE. WEMBLEY 1961)
GROUND: HAMPDEN AND EVERYWHERE ELSE
FANZINE: HAGGIS SUPPER (R.I.P)

* * *

First sung, I believe, by the Tartan Army in Vienna after an Austrian newspaper commented that the Scots liked to sing: 'And tonight we will hear the sound of music'.

DOH A DEER

Doh, a deer, a female deer,
Ray, a drop of golden sun,
Me, a name I call myself,

Fah, a long, long, way to run,
Soh, a needle pulling thread,
Lah, a note to follow soh,
Te, a drink with jam and bread
And that brings us back to doh, oh, oh, oh.

Then repeat until you drop dead or you need another pint, whichever comes first. We sang this for half an hour after we beat England in our last game at Wembley. God knows why, but we don't.

And the classic. It doesn't say what we will do when we arrive.

WE'RE COMING

We're coming, we're coming,
We're coming down the road.
When you hear the noise of the Tartan Army boys.
We'll be coming down the road.

. . . and repeat till your throat needs another beer. You are not drinking for fun, you know.

One for the Auld Enemy:

You're staying home, you're staying home

England's staying home
Three lions on your shirt, two goals in past Seaman
Fifteen pints last night, Gazza's fucking steaming
You're staying home, you're staying home
England's staying home

*

We hate Coca-Cola
We hate Fanta too . . . it's shite!
For we're the Tartan Army
And we drink Irn Bru

HERE WE GO

Here we go
Here we go
Here we go
Here we go
Here we go
Here we go
Here we go
Here we go
Here we go

and so on